To Mark

Longtime a friends - good to have you near and so caring,

Best,

Jerry

Professor Kittleman's Therapy

Professor Kittleman's Therapy

by Gerald Amada

Midnight Marquee Press, Inc.
Baltimore, Maryland, USA

ISBN 13: 978-1-887664-90-5
ISBN 10: 1-887664-90-4
Library of Congress Catalog Card Number 2009920569
Manufactured in the United States of America

First Printing by Midnight Marquee Press, Inc., February 2009

Dedication

To Kate Johnston

with appreciation

Well, I finally did it. After anguishing about it for weeks, I called Dr. Taub and made an appointment. His phone voice was pleasant, friendly; he said nothing offensive or off-putting. His East Coast accent sounded much like mine, which, according to some hairsplitting analysts, can foster interpersonal attunement. We'll see. In any event, I think I'll keep my appointment. Also, I'll send him a letter providing him with some biographical information that he may find useful in assisting me. Diary, how on earth do I account for the fact that I want to kill this man before I've ever really met him?

First Session 5/8/06

T: Professor Kittleman. Please come in, take a seat, make yourself comfortable. Did you find my office easily?

K: Yes, I did, thank you, Dr. Taub.

T: Well, then, why don't we get down to business. Please begin by telling me what brings you in. Start anywhere you like.

K: All right. But this won't be easy. I felt compelled to get professional help because something I did recently has caused me feelings of profound shame and self-contempt. These are feelings I can easily and directly attribute to my colossal gaffe, if we may call it that, but perhaps it would better serve the goals of therapy if I provided you with some background and context.

T: That's fine. Take whatever time you need. I imagine this won't be our final session.

K: Well, I'm an academic. I teach psychology at a local community college, not far from this office. I've been teaching for about 30 years and have enjoyed it immensely, although teaching in recent years has become arduous and even overwhelming at times because increasing numbers of students lack the requisite educational skills, motivation, and stick-to-itiveness to succeed academically. I don't of course entirely blame them for their academic shortcomings. Virtually everyone has let them down: their parents, the schools, the politicians (recall the president's educational agenda, which was so badly conceived and underfunded that his minions had to purchase media propaganda to prettify it for public marketing) and even many of the students' own peers, who prefer mall vagrancy and video games to reading books.

About 20 years ago or so I began to detect a decline, not only in college students' academic performance, but, commensurately, in their social behavior; toward one another and toward college officials, including their instructors. At first, it seemed like it was just the occasional oddball who came out of the woodwork and acted out of turn. But, gradually, my colleagues and I discerned a spreading contagion of ugly behavior among students who trespassed on the rights of others and whose disruptive behavior had a shattering effect upon the integrity of classroom instruction. True, some of the misconduct was rather innocuous; peccadilloes like chattering, falling asleep in class, and the loud snapping of chewing gum. Then the annoyances escalated, and, as they increased in number and severity, they took on more alarming forms of untoward conduct.

Students attempted to extort better grades by leveling menacing threats at instructors. Some of these students even enacted the threats by physically attacking instructors and administrators. A few years ago at my own campus a disgruntled student murdered one of our teachers in the classroom—cold-bloodedly gunned him down right in front of a large class of horrified and traumatized students. To this day no one seems to know why he committed the murder. For all I know, it could have been a mundane triviality such as receiving a C- on a test. They apprehended the culprit and he served a long prison sentence, but the murder sent shockwaves throughout the campus that did not subside for many years afterward. For example, many instructors and administrators were especially vigilant in sidestepping risky encounters with strange and volatile students even when the students were engaging is highly antisocial behavior at the time.

As well, some students contrive to sexually seduce their instructors in exchange for preferential treatment, also known as an inflated grade. To make matters worse, some instructors offer the quid pro quo of an inflated grade to select students for a choice platter of sexual favors. As if all of this wasn't bad enough, cheating, otherwise euphemistically known as plagiarism, has taken root and blossomed at colleges across the country. I know for a fact—the fact coming from the horse's mouth of a law school professor over lunch—that law students, who will soon be entering a profession known for its ethics and probity (of course, if we can only for the moment forget the corporate and political scandals that occur with some regularity and serve to taint our opinion of lawyers) are using their laptops in class to send messages to their classmates so they may correctly answer their professors' questions. You know, Dr. Taub, there's a researcher who has found that about 75 percent of all college students cheat within a given year. That, Dr. Taub, is more than half your students. I happen to know that because I took statistics in college. One more thing: did you know that 37 percent of all statistics are meaningless? Please pardon the lame attempt at humor in the midst of this grim subject. I read somewhere that humor is rightly considered to be one of the healthier, high-level defense mechanisms, which, knowing that, makes me feel a bit less defensive.

T: You're pardoned, but what do all these student high jinks have to do with your ghastly gaffe?

G: Everything. With all due respect, I must, in order to explain my life-transfiguring fiasco properly, be the voluble contextualist. Please allow me this luxury. After all, I'm merely obeying your advice to take what time I need to explain myself.

T: I'm sorry, please continue.

G: Actually, you're right. I'm being discursive. I'll move ahead. After surveying the problem of student misconduct at many schools and considering various remedial notions and potions, I cobbled together some central principles and strategies for dealing with disruption on campus. I published them in a health journal and then something happened that completely took me by surprise. I was invited to be a keynote speaker at a national conference, to address the problem of student misconduct. When I asked my hosts at the conference why they had selected me for this distinction, they told me that research and articles on the subject of college student misconduct were almost nonexistent and mine had been, in their view, truly trailblazing. I was flabbergasted by this news since I had not done a thorough review of the literature before I launched into writing my initial article.

Well, from that time forward I have been on the lecture circuit. I subsequently wrote a few fairly good books, received rather wide recognition as an authoritative and articulate speaker on the subject of student conduct issues, and have by now lectured at over 100 colleges in this country and Canada. It was the last college, my 112th, to be exact, that proved to be my downfall.

T: What happened, if I may ask?

K: Good timing. You certainly may ask and I, fortunately, possess the compulsion to tell you. The college is located in a suburban community in the Midwest. It has a deservedly good reputation based upon the excellent credentials and scholarly accomplishments of its faculty. After receiving a rather flattering introduction given by the provost, I sauntered up to the podium, adjusted the mike, spread out my notes and began my spiel.

I usually jump-start myself rather well by simply telling a short, inane joke or two because the joke telling works especially well as a serviceable net with which to catch and constrain some of the fluttering butterflies in my stomach. The audience ordinarily politely laughs, I wryly smile, and a good receptive mood is induced. On this occasion the audience seemed especially relaxed and attentive. Their collective approachability emboldened me and I was able to speak with genuine self-assurance and ease. My unselfconsciousness swept me along and I remember having a blithe feeling, an audacious presentiment if you will, that this lecture would receive high accolades from this audience of illustrious scholars.

T: But it never reached that pinnacle?

K: No, it did not. Just as I reached a point in the lecture where I needed to pause for reflection, a member of the audience let out a fart. I say, "let out." Perhaps I am not being accurate. Perhaps, instead, the fart, having been cruelly enslaved within the deeper recesses of the fart-maker's intestines for who knows how long, manumitted itself without proper authorization to do so. I don't know. In any event, I must say this particular flatus was no ordinary fart. Dr. Taub, please accept my apologies for this lapse into the scatological but I must describe this fart in some detail or what follows may not make great sense. The fart was many things: majestic, stentorian, bugle-military, effusive, protracted, preposterous, preternatural, buoyant, joyful, theatrical, and perhaps most importantly, it was very witty.

T: Witty?

G: Yes, witty. Why else would it have titillated the audience so much? Of course at first the audience was stunned into silence, awash with embarrassment and chagrin. But the silence was soon followed by a few innocent giggles, which quickly roiled and undulated into large waves of loud guffaws. Before I could say or do anything, practically the entire audience of these august savants was in an uproar, slapping their knees, pulling faces, and generally acting like a bunch of adolescents high on psychedelics. For more than a minute I stood there nonplussed, my mind suffused with flashing images and piercing impulses. I remember thinking I might score well with an old joke apropos of the fartfest taking place before me but, unlike the fart itself, it wouldn't come out. Then I thought I'd simply resume my talk and act as if nothing odd or special had happened.

But how could I resume a normal lecture under such circumstances? The fart had become the elephant in the room and I was no Clyde Beatty, a wild animal trainer extraordinaire who, with chair and whip at the ready, could tame the rampaging pachyderm. I found myself shriveling before my audience, aching with shame and humiliation, and wanting to flee at once to some unknown but distant refuge. Never before had I felt quite so trapped, so crushed, and so filled with ungovernable rage. My emotions were a blinding blizzard that froze me into a state of irreducible mental oblivion. Then, without at all realizing what I was doing, I stepped to the side of the podium, took a few more strides along the proscenium toward the audience and, finally halting at the edge of the forestage, stood there glaring at them for perhaps 10 seconds. It was then that I carried out my fateful act. I reached down, grabbed the zipper of my pants, pulled it down, reached into my underpants, groped my groin, and yanked out my penis for all to see.

I stood there in place, I'm now ashamed to say, without a trace of embarrassment or self-consciousness, as if I were proud of my phal-locentric tour de force. Needless to say, the audience was immediately thunderstruck into a collective silence, aghast over this obscene spectacle. Within a matter of just a few seconds, however, a few of the women in the audience let out bloodcurdling screams and some of the men thrust their clenched fists into the air and made menacing gestures that reminded me of the lynching mob that strung up Dana Andrews in *The Ox-Bow Incident*. Without any question, this group of normally staid instructors was really wrought-up and hankering for revenge. Of what kind I pre-ferred not to imagine.

Well, I guess the thought of an outbreak of mayhem also occurred to the provost because he darted over to me, grabbed me by the arm, and pulled me from the stage while rasping into my ear, "Zip it up. Goddamn it, zip it up, you fucking wacko. What the hell has gotten into you? They were only giggling over a fart, not execrating your ancestry."

I was taken to the office of campus security where a fairly benign interrogation took place. The chief of security and the provost mulled over two unpalatable (to me) courses of action: to have me prosecuted and jailed for public exposure or arrange for mandatory psychiatric hospitalization based upon the criterion that I was a danger to myself (and possibly to others). By expressing the utmost contrition for my actions and promising to get to the root of my "problem" and cure it through psychotherapy, I was somehow able to convince them simply to let me go home on my own, providing, of course, that I never set foot on their campus again.

By the time I returned to my college the news of my debacle had made its way along the inter-collegiate grapevine to the extent that my career as a lecturer on, of all things, student misconduct and incivility, suffered a quick and certain quietus. Fortunately, my own college thought I posed no particular danger to its students, so they kept me on, although I know I have been watched pretty closely for any signs of demented malfeasance that might yet be in my mental repertoire.

Well, Dr. Taub, there it is. I have, after enjoying a splendid career as a nationally recognized lecturer, torpedoed my life's work, exposed myself to calumny and ridicule wherever I go, at least in academic circles, and shredded my self-respect beyond recognition and repair—all in a moment of fitful exhibitionism. Tell me, can you help me? Is there anything you can do to make things better? Or perhaps a better question might be: is there anything you might do that could make things worse?

T: I seriously doubt the latter possibility. I'd like to be given the opportunity to help you. I think you might find it very beneficial for the two of us to closely examine and understand the many complicated causes, rooted in both your past as well as your current life, that brought on that moment of "fitful exhibitionism," as you call it. If we can do that on a regular basis and in a gradual, systematic way, in time you may find you will reach the point of being more self-forgiving and self-respecting. For now, our time is about up. I will see you on Thursday at two o'clock. Take care, Dr. Kittleman.

T: You, too, Dr. Taub.

Professor Kittleman's Diary 5/8/06

The session went very well, I thought. Of course I would think it went well; I'm a fitful, narcissistic exhibitionist and I did the lion's share of talking. Arnold Taub, Ph.D., appears to be a man of about 60 years of age. He struck the appropriate balance of reserve and warmth throughout the session and deserves my appreciation for his evenly hovering attentiveness, as Freud might put it. The fact that he was neither shocked nor discombobulated by my scandalous tale was a gauge, in my view, of his emotional maturity and extensive professional experience. I particularly liked his eyes; they seemed at once sad, contemplative, empathic, and yet wry. He is plainspoken, and chooses his soft words in a careful, unstilted, and purposeful manner—in my estimation this manner constitutes an essential quality in a therapist's professional armamentarium. I hope the psoriasis on his left hand is not a psychosomatic condition. I'd like to think, however unrealistically, that he is a paragon of emotional health. The ring on that psoriatic hand seems to emblematize heterosexual marriage, but one can never take such things for granted. Frankly, I don't much care about his sexual orientation one way or the other as long as he, gay or straight, keeps his erotic urges in check. The office is conventionally and tastefully furnished and boasts a few African woodcarvings that, due to their vivid grotesquerie, at times distracted me during our session. I suppose these carvings are some of the procurements of Dr. Taub's worldwide travels. There is an analytic couch in the room, but I prefer that the therapy be conducted face-to-face and am pleased that Dr. Taub does too. Diary, I find it interesting that my largely favorable impressions of him notwithstanding, my homicidal feelings toward this man underwent a discernible upsurge during and since our first session.

Dr. Taub's Anamnesis 5/8/06

The patient, Professor Sheldon Kittleman, teaches psychology at a local college. According to the data he enclosed in his letter to me prior to our first session, he is a widower, age 62, who has taught college for about 30 years. As he gained prominence in the field of student disciplinary issues he began to publish books and articles on this subject that enabled him to gain national prominence as a public speaker. Until recently, he had been lecturing on a regular basis at colleges and universities throughout the country. On what he aptly calls a "fateful" day, he publicly exposed his genitals to a faculty audience after they had uproariously laughed over a very audible fart that had been emitted by one of the attendees. His act of public exposure has virtually ended his career as an on-the-circuit lecturer but, fortunately, did not cause his dismissal from his own college. He is, as one might expect, still reverberating from the shattering effects of this extremely painful experience by manifesting a fairly severe depression.

Professor Kittleman, again according to his written account, is an only child. His parents emigrated from Galicia, Poland, in the early part of the past century. His father was a dry cleaner and his mother a homemaker. Evidently, the Kittleman family led a hardscrabble life in Newark, New Jersey, along with most of the other families in their working-class neighborhood. His father died in a nursing home about 10 years ago at the age of 95. His mother died about 35 years ago from congestive heart failure.

Professor Kittleman's wife, Ethel, died approximately eight years ago when she was struck by a car as she was jaywalking across a busy thoroughfare near their home. The driver of the vehicle was a neighbor of the Kittlemans, a Mr. Arthur Semmel. The Semmels and the Kittlemans had known each other for many years and were such fast friends that they even went on vacations together each summer. Many of their get-togethers afterward were devoted to reminiscing about these glorious vacations spent in such far-flung places as Yellowstone, Grand Canyon, Key West, Aruba, and Quebec. When Mr. Semmel learned that Ethel Kittleman had died in the hospital soon after the car accident he went into virtual seclusion, encumbered his conscience with massive guilt, and lived in monastic solitude until his death about a year later. So, within a single year, Sheldon Kittleman had lost his wife and his best friend. Now and

Professor Kittleman's Therapy 15

then he and Semmel's wife, Valerie, talk on the phone but their conversations, according to the patient's written account, are marked by a frosty sterility that smacks of mutual mourning, distrust, and a welter of hidden resentments—all of this amounting to a kind of truceless and inviolable pact of recognition that each blames, and always will blame, the other's spouse for the tragically premature death of his own spouse. The patient disclosed in his letter that he and his wife had never had children; there was no word of explanation or elaboration attached to this fact.

The patient stated matter-of-factly that he is in excellent physical health.

Initial diagnostic impression: The patient is suffering from a moderate to severe depression based upon the recent upheaval in his professional career that has suddenly deprived him of a rich source of accomplishment, fulfillment, public recognition and, more problematically, his self-respect and self-esteem. It is probable that this wrenching personal loss has revivified his most intense feelings of grief over the sudden and decidedly premature death of his wife, with whom, he convincingly states, he enjoyed many years of love and close companionship. Based on the patient's outlandish act of exhibitionism, I would conjecture that his is a narcissistic personality with the rather classic traits that accompany this personality type: self-inflation (just how grandiose remains to be seen), devaluation of others, and, inter alia, an overweening sense of self-entitlement.

The patient indicates that he wishes to be seen on a weekly basis and I have consented to this arrangement with the proviso that we periodically evaluate the advisability of weekly sessions. Although he has never before been in psychotherapy, he seems particularly amenable to receiving psychoanalytically oriented treatment (he mentioned in his letter that this was a modality he favored and was one of the reasons he chose me, through a friend's referral, as his therapist) and gives early indication that he will make productive use of our sessions. I have tabled the subject of psychotropic medications for the time being in order to test the patient's capacity for using interpretations, support, an empathic holding environment, and insight to cope with his depression. Besides, he also told me in his letter that he had chosen to see a psychologist rather than a psychiatrist because he is averse to dealing with his problems by taking meds and was fearful that a psychiatrist might be an all-too-eager pill dispenser.

T: Where would you like to begin?

K: I don't know. Do you have any suggestions?

T: Normally, I would leave that up to you, but perhaps it might help if you could tell me your thoughts about the incident that precipitated your need to seek therapy. Was this incident entirely unprecedented or have you ever experienced anything like it before?

K: That's a good, evocative question. I'll let my thoughts drift for a moment and then tell you where they have taken me. (A pause of about 30 seconds.) Okay. I'm perhaps taking your question too literally, but I'll start by telling you two other experiences in my life when my penis got me into serious trouble. Perhaps they're related to the recent one, perhaps not.

The first took place when I was about 15 years old and attending junior high school. I was taking first-year Spanish with Mrs. Martinez, a short, round, matronly woman who kept her students in tow by excitedly yelling at them every few minutes. When she spoke calmly and quietly, her Spanish accent sounded deliciously musical and captivating. However, her repeated outbursts of ugly temper caused her to berate her turned-off students with pejorative slurs that were meant to and did cause emotional wounds. Words like "stupid," "illiterate," and "lazy" were a regular and indispensable part of her vocabulary.

My test grades in Spanish were consistently mediocre but I was definitely on my way to passing the course when I was waylaid by a breast. I should emphasize that this was no ordinary breast. The breast belonged to Benicia Nelson, the black voluptuary who sat in the seat one row in front of me. Each day, from one to two o'clock, I clandestinely eyeballed and thirsted over the lovely curves of her coal-black body. Benicia, in her tight white blouse and even tighter blue skirt, was bursting with nubility and I, who had never even kissed a girl (except once, when a bottle happened to spin my way at a Halloween party), had ecstatic visions of ravaging her beautiful black body in the most extraordinary venues: the Tarzan tree house (the one I saw in the movies), an airplane cockpit, the home team dugout at Yankee Stadium, the cloakroom at the rear of our classroom (to save time), my parents' bed, the couch of my old rabbi's office—well, you get the idea, Dr. Taub, anywhere my lewd imagination would take me…and Benicia. The more perverse and desecrating the reverie, the merrier the imagined sex.

Well, one day Benicia overtempted my prurience for her. While Mrs. Martinez had become preoccupied with some work at her desk, Benicia turned to her friend in the next seat and began a funny, bantering conversation that was chock-full of sexual innuendo. Each would tease the other about some of the boys they knew and had played around with. In fairly blunt terms they began trading disclosures about how far they had gone, although, of course, leaving out the most sordid details. As they capered along in this way, I felt myself literally warming to the occasion. My shirt was soon wet with concupiscent sweat. My sexual urges were definitely aflame and completely ready to consume Benicia right there on her desk. My envy of the boys who had gone far with these two alluring girls was also aroused and further fueled my desire for Benicia.

Then the fun really began. The girls began to use Spanish words they had learned in this class, but assigned to them certain sexual connotations that lifted them entirely out of context and dropped them into an erotic cauldron. For example, I can still remember Benicia saying to her friend, "If you don't like it, girl, you can kiss my *cadera*." Her friend's riposte to the "*cadera*" remark was, "Well, if you don't like it, Benicia, you can suck my Titicaca." (Just that day Mrs. Martinez had mentioned that lake, which straddles Peru and Bolivia, and evidently its singular name had struck and adhered to the friend's funny bone.) With every exchange of this witty repartee each girl let out a howl of laughter and congratulated the other for her cleverness.

Benicia, however, went a step further. She periodically turned to her friend to give her a light, comradely poke on the arm. As she did, her underarm and the upper part of her left breast were exposed. I could see the breast, as it jiggled within its loose bra, almost to its areola. This was clearly too much for a sexual novitiate like myself. I had been transported, air-expressed to a voyeur's heaven where pretty, chocolate-colored girls were regaling me with suggestive words and mammiferous enticements.

I was now faced with a serious dilemma. I was fully and visibly tumescent and class would be over in about five minutes. I could hardly leave my seat in such an erectile state; surely, I'd become a laughingstock of the school. I would be known overnight by my schoolmates as Sheldon Boner and I'd never live it down.

In my mind's eye I could even see the words beneath my picture in the school yearbook: "In his first year Sheldon was almost a goner. But in his second year he rose to the challenge by becoming a boner."

Then, the worst possible thing that could happen happened. Mrs. Martin decided to use the remaining five minutes of class for an exercise in conjugating a verb. She searched the room for a student to come up to the blackboard for this exercise and her covetous eyes fell upon, of all people, me. "Sheldon, please come up to the board," she said, plying me with a gentle voice and manner. What could I say to escape this impending calamity? Could I perhaps dissuade her by saying, "I'm sorry, Mrs. Martinez, but I have a rather large erection at the moment and am indisposed? Perhaps you could call on me tomorrow when I won't be so aroused and projective."

Cornered, I knew instinctively what I had to do. I said I couldn't conjugate the verb and therefore didn't want to come to the front of the class. Mrs. Martinez would not take no for an answer and insisted that I obey her. I again refused and then leapt out of my chair, turned my body in the direction of the wall to my right, and bolted from the room. Later that day my mother received a phone call from the vice principal informing her that I had been suspended from Spanish and would be given a failing grade for the term. I could, if I wished, make up the lost term in high school the following year. My parents were scandalized by my uncharacteristic display of hooliganism and un-Jewish behavior but, frankly, to me the suspension was a less Draconian measure than having to stand up in front of 30 students and showcase my boner.

T: So you went through an experience as an adolescent that is similar in at least one respect to your recent "fitful act of exhibitionism."

K: How so, Dr. Taub?

T: You felt trapped. You were overwhelmed by circumstantial pressures to perform in a socially acceptable but constricted manner, but the fart and the erection allowed you no viable recourse, no escape. You then felt compelled to mutiny, so to speak.

K: Yes, I suspect you are quite right. There are many times when I feel that I am caught in a maelstrom of entrapments. My life, especially since I lost my wife, who was both a helpmate and a mooring anchor, has been lived within a Sartreian labyrinth that communicates with no exit. Within the labyrinth I try, of course, to seek meaning, truth, and justice, but only with partial success, I'm afraid.

T: Would you care to tell me any more about the outcome of your lost term in that Spanish class? Did it cause you any particular hardship?

K: Funny you should ask. I enrolled in high school Spanish in my second term. My teacher, Ms. Solis, was a bright, flamboyant and tongue-lashing spitfire. She, like her predecessor, lost no opportunity to assail the slower students with deprecations that must have caused a few of them gnawing self-doubts that took years of therapy to overcome. In any event, I was cowed by her and my lack of confidence resulted in, once again, substandard grades. After being targeted in a particularly blistering way by her one afternoon for my failure to complete an assignment, I went home and mulled over my choices. Should I remain in the class, languish there for the remainder of the term, and complete Spanish with a poor grade? Or, quit the class, wait until the following term and take the other Spanish teacher, who had a reputation for softer, more compassionate teaching? Or, bow my neck, embark on a course of serious study and see how far my innate intelligence and new academic regimen could take me? The third option seemed the most inviting since I stood to gain the most by improving my work then and there in order to reap a better grade coupled with the opportunity to complete Spanish within a single year.

So I buckled down and, using a bit of ingenuity, I came upon a surefire method of success. Ms. Solis each day assigned the class homework that entailed a summary translation of short passages from the textbook. Most of the students, including myself, considered the assignment a pushover and handled it quite well, although I occasionally botched it badly by mistranslating, and then misconstruing, a few pivotal words. It occurred to me that I could surpass my classmates by raising the requirements of the assignment one notch higher; I would, on my own volition, fully translate—that is, word for word—the textbook passages that everyone else was only summarizing. It would take much longer and be god-awful tedious, but I knew Ms. Solis would be pleasantly surprised, if not shocked, by my sudden scholastic turnabout.

My moment in the sun came the very next day. Ms. Solis called upon three students in succession to summarize a few paragraphs from the textbook. Then she asked me to do the same. Sheldon Boner would rise to the challenge, but this time another organ—the second most important one, according to Woody Allen—would enable me to take intellectual command. I translated every single word of a page-long paragraph. As I proceeded I noticed that the usual student rustling of papers had subsided and everyone was staring at me intently, especially the nonplussed Ms. Solis. When I had completed my translation, she simply stood there wide-eyed and speechless for all of perhaps half a minute. Then, regaining her composure, she thanked me for my good work and went on to another student, who reverted to summarizing a passage from the book.

Each day for the next two weeks, whenever Ms. Solis called upon me to read from the textbook, I did a verbatim translation. Oddly, although my classmates could see how my virtuoso performances were placing them at an academic disadvantage in the eyes of Ms. Solis, not one of them attempted to emulate me in this respect. They somehow thought it best to stick to their summarizations. During those two weeks I felt like a different person; someone with promise and potential who could amount to something if I could only continue to apply myself as I was doing in Ms. Solis's class. For the first time in my life I began to think of myself as bright and educable and, perhaps most importantly, it seemed that, if I played my cards right, I could be the master and arbiter of my own destiny, if that isn't a too extravagant way of describing the feelings of a callow kid of 16.

Well, I'm afraid, Dr. Taub, all of my spirit and momentum came to an end in a trice, ripped away from me by the ineptitude and revolting cynicism of a teacher who had a much-touted gift for languages but also, evidently, a genius for strangling the inchoate hopes and dreams of one of her students.

T: To what are you referring, if I may ask?

K: I'm referring to something that happened in the third week of my zesty feats of translation. As I was strolling along the school corridors between classes a close friend of mine called out to me: "Hey, Sheldon, I want to ask you something. You're taking Ms. Solis for Spanish, aren't you?" I told him I was and asked why he wanted to know. "Well, she buttonholed me in the hallway a couple of days ago. You know, I took her for Spanish last term and was one of the better students in her class." "Yeah, but what's that got to do with me?," I wanted to know. He smiled and said, "I'll tell you what it has to do with you. Right out of the blue she asks me if I am doing your homework for you. She said something about a big and sudden improvement in your translations. She thought, since I had been one of her good students last term and, knowing we were good friends from seeing us together a lot at school, that I was perhaps coaching or even cheating for you. If I'm not mistaken, there was a threatening tone to her comments." "What did you tell her?" "I told her the truth, Sheldon, that I didn't know anything about your translations." "Did she seem to believe you, Larry?" "To tell you the truth, Sheldon, I don't think she did. Well, maybe she doesn't necessarily think I'm your partner in crime, but I think, judging by that dubious expression on her face, she believes someone is carrying your ass in Spanish. You don't have to answer this, Sheldon, but is someone doing your Spanish translations for you?" I looked at my best friend with disgust and said, "Larry, you know I haven't been a particularly good student, but I've never been a dishonest student. That's all I've got to say." With that, I walked quickly away from him. We remained good friends throughout high school but his interrogative assailing my integrity and intellectual capabilities took a large bite out of my respect for him.

T: Understandably so. So, how did you deal with Ms. Solis after she had betrayed you in such a vile way?

K: The words "betrayal" and "vile" hit the bull's eye of my feelings toward her then and now. I appreciate your apt use of them, Dr. Taub. Anyway, I returned to Spanish class a sullen and incorrigible student. The next time I was called upon to translate, I stumblingly summarized a passage and when I finished I glared at Ms. Solis with unmistakable hatred in my eyes. She, in response, stared back, but to my surly delight, she quickly and nervously averted her eyes from mine and went on with her lesson plan in a visibly agitated manner. For the remainder of the term I became a "summarizer" and, for my lame academic efforts, received a C in the course. You might logically ask, Dr. Taub, why I did not speak up, say something to Ms. Solis about her hideous behavior toward me.

T: Yes, you've preempted me Dr. Kittleman. I was about to ask you just that question.

K: Good. The answer, Dr. Taub, is a simple and straightforward one. I was not the kind of kid who could do something like that. I was a "good" kid who was taught by his parents to be docile and compliant in the company of adults. I wasn't just afraid to defy or openly disagree with adults, but the mere thought of actually defying an adult in a direct and angry manner was nowhere to be found in my mental armamentarium. In other words, there was simply nothing in my brain to tap or use for capital when dealing with mean and nutty adults. And, as you in particular well know, mean and nutty adults are everywhere, causing vulnerable children untold misery. So, I, one of those vulnerable kids, could only sit there and stare at Ms. Solis, but never tell her what I really thought of her.

T: You said "actually" defying an adult. Why did you express yourself that way?

K: Because I had, and still have, thank goodness, a fervid fantasy life. My fantasies have succored and rescued me time and time again when I have had to deal with despicable people.

T: How, specifically?

K: Well, let's take Ms. Solis, for example. After this sorry episode in Spanish class, I had many glorious fantasies of torturing and killing her. The thought of acting on these fantasies was, fortunately, too horrific to contemplate, but the fantasies themselves were always deliciously retributive and, because they seemed to mete out a form of sublime justice, they sustained me as I served prison time in that despicable teacher's classroom for a few more months. You know, Dr. Taub, whenever I have thought about this teacher over the ensuing years, I wondered what she ultimately thought of my second turnabout in her class, you know, the sudden nosedive I took when I went back to summarizing the assigned pages. Did she think, on the one hand, that I gave up my full translations because she had caught me cheating red-handed and surmised that I no longer wanted to keep up a cheap sham? Or did she, on the other hand, surmise the truth: that my pride, my zeal for learning and self-betterment, and my sunshiny days of stellar achievement in her class had all suddenly gone up in smoke because they had been torched by her cynical aspersion on my character? Of course, I'll never know the answer to that conundrum, Dr. Taub, but something tells me that Ms. Solis salved her conscience by convincing herself that I was an unregenerate plagiarist. Anyway, you can now see, Dr. Taub, how my penis uprisings have been instrumental in shaping my life, not to speak of the contours of the crotch of my pants.

T: This "sorry episode," as you put it, seems to represent yet another experience in which you felt trapped, squelched, but unable to escape circumstances beyond your control. The rage you felt had no safety valve that would offer comfort, validation or retribution, except in your fantasies. You went through great pain, humiliation, and disillusionment when your intellectual achievements—and your very integrity—were questioned and invalidated by Ms. Solis's attributing them to your friend. In Mrs. Martinez's class you were deprived of the power of words to explain your erection predicament, since a disclosure of the truth would obviously have brought on further shame and humiliation. It posed another inescapable situation. I'm afraid our time is up for today. Would you care to briefly comment, however, on what I have just said?

K: You have apparently discerned a significant theme that is emerging in my discursive blatherings here, Dr. Taub. I will give it serious consideration. By the way, I just realized that there were two penis tales I had promised to tell you and I've only told one. Well, see you next week.

5/12/06 Professor Kittleman's Diary

How can I tell if my use of therapy is productive or not? I acknowledge, diary, that I can be discursive and hyperbolic in narrating my life, but isn't my style of communication, along with everything else about me, grist for Dr. Taub's therapeutic mill? I must say without equivocation that this last session provided me with a welcome catharsis. I feel better for having told Dr. Taub about my two Spanish teachers. They say that one of the great benefits of psychotherapy is the opportunity it affords the patient to share grievous intimacies that have never before been shared with anyone and, as a kind of bonus, also provides a safe haven from harsh judgment. I think I can already vouch for these benefits. Having said all those nice things about therapy and Dr. Taub, I am acutely aware of periodic urges to kill him; before, during, and after sessions. I know that I will eventually tell him about these urges, but I probably won't for quite a while. It's just too discomfiting at present.

The patient discussed his childhood experiences in two different Spanish classes, one in middle school, the second in high school. The experiences are linked because his failure to complete the first course led to his placement in the second one a full term behind his closest friend and other classmates. This friend became implicated in an incident that caused the patient great humiliation and an academic setback. The main culprit in the tale told by the patient is a Spanish teacher who indirectly accused him of academic deceit and plagiarism. She remains a villainous person in the patient's gallery of thwarting and dehumanizing individuals; his wrathful feelings toward her remain, even after many years, quite intense. The session began, however, with an earlier experience in which the patient's erotic arousal in a junior high classroom made him flee, thus causing him to be suspended.

The narcissistic blows to Professor Kittleman's sense of self are evident throughout the first two sessions. Each narrated experience seems exemplified by psychologically entrapping circumstances from which he could not extricate himself or find a voice with which to defend or advocate for himself. Thus, he came away from each experience with a badly damaged or impotent sense of self.

At the present time the transference appears to be rather positive but I suspect that we will see clearer manifestations of a negative transference as the patient begins to feel insufficiently acknowledged or appreciated by me.

K: I suppose, Dr. Taub, I should begin where I left off. I promised to tell you my second penis tale. Would you mind?

T: Please go ahead, if you'd like.

K: I was a junior in college. On weekends, after a dull week of hunkering down with our books, my friends and I would go out foraging far and wide for girls, usually without, I must confess, great success. On this one occasion, Roger and I decided to go into New York, to Central Park where we heard they had popular outdoor dances that were free. After wandering about the asphalt dance floor in search of a receptive, pretty face, I spotted one very much to my liking. By that time my friend had already found a comely mate and was dancing with her.

I walked over to a girl who was quite alone and whose eyes seemed to be panning the crowd for a dance partner. Steeling myself against my usual fear that my offer to dance would be gruffly declined, I quickly popped the obligatory question, "Would you care to dance?" while flashing an artificially cheerful smile. The girl smiled back appreciatively, did not say yes, but firmly took my hand, and led me out onto the dance floor, all without a hint of pretension or guile. This definitely was not my usual experience, I can assure you, Dr. Taub. If girls actually agreed to dance with me their usual manner was marked by a crusty, stand-offish air that Morse-signaled a message that an arctic headwind was coming in my direction and should be decoded to read: "I may be accepting this dance but don't expect anything more from me, not even another dance. So don't get any foolish notions in your head that you're going to get in my pants, not tonight, not ever."

Once on the dance floor Eva and I wrapped our arms around each other in the standard way and I clumsily attempted to calibrate the proper extent of physical closeness we should assume by reading her body language. I was, however, shocked to discover, almost immediately, that Eva was no friend of calibration. In no time at all she moved—no, that's too tame a word—she shoved her crotch tightly against mine and no sooner did I become hard, she repeatedly surged into my erection as we danced. I returned the thrusts without concern for how our animal gyrations appeared to others since the dance floor had markedly darkened in the gloaming and the park lights were quite weak.

Eva and I danced many times that starlit night in the park. While we danced we hardly spoke to each other. Nothing mattered but the sensuality of the moment. When "Good Night Sweetheart" was played, spelling the end of the dance, we held hands and went in search of Roger and his dance partner. Roger drove the girls, who happened to be friends and had come together to the dance, to their homes in midtown Manhattan. Eva gave me her phone number and asked me to call. After we dropped the girls off Roger and I went out for a snack at a late-night hamburger joint in New Jersey. After we went in and sat down I grabbed a napkin and was about to put it on my lap when I saw something that absolutely horrified me. On my pants was a huge whitish, crystalline stain that must have covered at least half the front of my pants. My first thought was that I had inadvertently and unknowingly spilled something into my lap; milk perhaps. I touched it and it was dry, so I deduced that the stain was made much earlier in the evening. Then I realized, to my horror, what had really happened. I had come in my pants while snuggled against Eva and hadn't even known it! In any case, there was no way I was going to share the secret of my seminal attainment with Roger. Crouching over, I left the eatery well in front of him and right after I got home I washed my pants before my mother could inspect them and have a cataleptic fit. A couple of days later I called Eva to set our first date.

T: Well, Dr. Kittleman, unlike the other experiences you've described, this time your penis didn't undermine your prospects for a good relationship with a desirable young woman. As a matter of fact, perhaps it served you well in arousing her sensual interest in you.

K: Perhaps you're right, Dr. Taub. She certainly could not help feeling my erection pressed against her, yet I seriously doubt she could have seen or known about the spillage from my ejaculation. So this story seems to have a good ending. But, alas, it does not.

T: No? Why not?

K: Well, at first my only reservation about dating Eva had to do with the long schlep from Newark to her home in Manhattan, first by bus, then the Hudson Tubes, and, then, to polish off the last leg of the trip, the New York subway system. At the time I had no car of my own and couldn't rely on Roger for transportation since he didn't want to date the girl he had met at the dance. The travel time and expense put a strain on my tight schedule and, even more, on my financial resources, but the dates went extremely well and in a matter of only a few weeks I realized that I had a steadfast "girlfriend" whom I could count on seeing each weekend. This was enormously reassuring to a guy who had gnawing doubts about his desirability as a "boyfriend" and, as an added reward, it put a happy end to the aimless and unsuccessful forays I made with my friends to dances and social events looking for girls.

The dates quickly settled into a very pleasant but highly idiosyncratic pattern. Eva's father, whom I was never to meet, evidently bore me, and perhaps all of Eva's past and future suitors, a nasty grudge. He informed her, in no uncertain terms, that he didn't want her to date me, an obviously predatory stranger, who came over from New Jersey looking for loose girls. She was a mature 17, almost 18, so it seemed, at least to me, that he had stretched his parental prerogatives well beyond their legitimate bounds. Eva, who had a recalcitrant streak, concocted a subterfuge that worked to perfection. Whenever we set up a date, she told her father that she was going out with a girlfriend. We then planned to meet at a specified time and street corner for each of our dates. I usually arrived early and almost invariably, while cooling my heels on the street corner, would be solicited by a bedraggled panhandler. Disregarding my financial straits, I always managed to dole out some change, but never without a social expectation. I would corral the supplicant into conversation. The topic was unimportant as long as the conversation lasted until Eva arrived. Most of the panhandlers were regulars on that corner and since I had come to be known and celebrated as an easy touch, I got to know some of them pretty well, and of course vice versa.

My conversations with these men achieved two self-serving purposes. First, they enabled me to deal with the tedium of standing alone on an impersonal street with nothing to do but spectate the passers-by. But more importantly, it seemed to charm and amuse Eva that, each time we met she found me in animated conversation with a forsaken vagrant. She evidently appreciated my natural equalitarianism as I hobnobbed with the scorned and contemned of the city, something I did without conde-scension or affectation. And I enjoyed it when Eva teased me by saying something like, "You know, Sheldon, I think you come to New York only to meet these poor vagrants, not date me. Since you like them so much, why don't we take some of them with us on our dates?"

The dates, as I've said, went well. Most of the time we went to see a movie in the neighborhood. Actually, we saw very little of the movies. Instead, we selected seats in a secluded, unpeopled corner of the theater and spent most of the time smooching. Do you want to hear something funny, Dr. Taub? Before I had even dated Eva she had gyrated between my legs in public and I had had a standing orgasm while planted between hers. But throughout the entire time we dated, I never went that far with her again. Of course the hot kissing and embracing at the movies was truly voluptuous, but circumstances—after all, we could never go anywhere that afforded us ironclad privacy and I was too shy to suggest a hotel room—prevented us from properly consummating our frenzied dance in Central Park. But it was not for lack of screwing that brought our relationship to an end.

T: No? What was it, then?

K: Something far more complicated, distressing, and regrettable. It was the fact that she was not Jewish and I am.

T: She wasn't an anti-Semite, was she? After all, she had dated you for quite a while.

K: No, it was nothing like that. But I need to explain. You see, I never told her I was a Jew and she never asked me anything about my ethnicity or religion. Of course my name must have given me away, but the subject simply didn't come up. I knew of course that she was a Gentile, a Catholic. I had no objections to dating or even marrying a non-Jew, if it came to that. But I had no way of knowing how she felt or how her father, who already had me pegged as a reprobate, would accept the fact that I was a member of the race that had killed his savior, at least according to the anti-Semitic indictments I had often heard as a kid. After all, even some of my closest Catholic friends repeated this rubbish, this ancient shibboleth, after having heard it from the mouths of Jew-hating nuns and priests at their church.

I wanted to tell Eva about my being Jewish, but somehow couldn't. I feared that a disclosure of this kind might cause her to turn away from me. Perhaps she would think I objected to her Catholicism. Or, she would own up and tell me that, although she always knew I was a Jew, she could abide it for a while because she would never allow the relationship to become more serious than it was, due to our religious differences. Now that I had made an issue of it, it was time for us to part ways. And I simply could not face the possibility that I would be spurned because I was a Jew.

I handled this quandary in the manner in which I handled all such quandaries: badly. I allowed many days to go by before calling Eva. She wanted to know what had happened since we had made a tentative date for the following weekend. I deflected her question by vaguely blaming my sudden, inexplicable disappearance on a busy academic schedule; tests, papers, homework. The tremulous edge and many hesitations in her speech clearly bespoke a restrained incredulousness that I found unbearable. I told her I couldn't talk for long but promised to get back to her. I called again the following week only to repeat the same malarkey. She was resignedly quiet and I thought I heard the kind of snuffling that accompanies a sob. She merely said she would wait for my next call. There was no next call. It was over between Eva and me and I hated myself for what I had done to her.

T: You never saw again?

K: Once, Dr. Taub. A couple of months later I wrote to her and told her the whole story, including a highly self-flagellating elucidation of all my cowardly thoughts and deeds. I apologized profusely for hurting her and truthfully assured her that she deserved someone better than me. And I made it absolutely clear that I now fully realized that my fears that she would react adversely to an open discussion that confronted the matter of what my Jewishness meant to our relationship were entirely irrational, and most likely related to some core feeling in me, not her, that was perversely anti-Semitic.

A few days later I received a temperate and heart-rending letter from Eva. She pointed out that, before meeting me, she had dated other Jewish boys and always gotten along well with them. In a tone that was entirely free of criticism and vituperation, she pointed out that I had made a colossal mistake in misjudging her so badly. Of course, she had always assumed that I was Jewish and had looked forward to the time when we might tackle the matter of our ethnic and religious differences, especially if we intended to become more serious about our common future. Unlike me, she had welcomed the opportunity to deepen our ties by courageously facing such challenges together.

I carefully perused this letter for signs of a door ajar enough to lead us down a corridor toward reconciliation. The words and the tone of the letter were at best neutral and non-committal on this score. I let a few months go by before calling Eva. I asked if she would like to spend the day browsing about my college campus with me. She was agreeable, but not effusively so. I borrowed a car from one of my friends, picked her up at the usual street corner, and we drove back to New Jersey. In the car our conversation was stilted. She no longer lavished me with smiles let alone kisses. She let me do most of the talking and I rambled on about subjects that interested neither of us. She sat at the far end of the passenger seat, pressed against the door as if immediate egress might be necessary at any moment. Things didn't get any better when we arrived on campus. She seemed preoccupied, said little about the college and evinced almost no personal interest in me.

When I suggested in the afternoon that I take her home she seemed relieved and on the way back to New York she relaxed a bit, chatted amiably and seemed to be her old self, I suppose because we had managed to get through the entire day without a rancorous exchange of words and without, I might add, the least bit of intimacy. When I dropped her off she thanked me for a nice day, bounded out of the car like a jackrabbit that had just been freed from its cage and waved to me as I drove away. I never saw or heard from her again.

T: We'll have to stop now but I'd like to ask you a question about your experience with Eva. You were enormously apprehensive about telling her you were Jewish. That caused you to do things, or fail to do things, that represented in your own estimation a failure of character on your part and you suffered greatly for these mistakes. Even now, your tears and evident sadness convey how much this memory of your time with Eva many years ago still pains you. Perhaps in our next session you could explain why being Jewish had become so abhorrent to you that you had to keep it a well-guarded secret from Eva.

K: There's much I can say about that, Dr. Taub, and, now that you've inquired about it, I'll be quite willing to discuss it further in our next session. Thanks. Goodbye.

Professor Kittleman's Diary 5/21/06

Diary, I did not feel at all well after this session. For two days I was distraught over my egregious mistreatment of Eva. Of course I realize that over time she probably has found a good man, married, had kids, and led a reasonably contented life. What's more, she probably has completely forgotten that I was ever a part of her life. I find it hard to believe that she could imagine that I would be discussing her in a therapy session, where I spend $110 a pop, almost 50 years after our groins met in crepuscular Central Park.

As for Dr. Taub, he is a good, patient listener. I suppose any therapist who had the grievous misfortune to be mine would have to be a good listener; I'm so damned garrulous and circumstantial. I wonder if he is bored. I look for signs of woolgathering in his apparently interested eyes and so far have seen none. After the session I harbored two equally strong and contradictory feelings toward him. On the positive side, I appreciated his willingness to hear me out without prodding me with intrusive interpretations or rescuing gestures of empathy. I am also exceedingly grateful for his open validation of feelings that harked back to 50-year-old events. His kind acknowledgement of the pain connected with my long-buried memories swept away a nagging worry that he might all at once crush me with a thoughtless comment like, "You know, what happened then took place a long time ago. Don't you think it's time you got over it?"

On the negative side, in telling him about my monumental, impulsive blunders, I've exposed my many vulnerabilities to a complete stranger who could misuse them for some malevolent purpose, such as humiliating me with judgmental opinions about them, if and when he so chooses. After all, I don't know and never will really know Dr. Taub. Yes, professional ethics require that he treat me with the utmost respect and sensitivity, but he is a human being (and to paraphrase Mark Twain, there is nothing worse that can be said about a person) and that means he has a dark side, a place in his psyche where dwell many of the same demons that are chasing me to perdition. It is these doubts, I'm convinced, that incite my murderous feelings for him. For now, I know these feelings are well under control, but, let's face it, diary, I'm the guy who disgorged his penis from his underpants in front of 200 astonished people who were expecting to hear me advise them about how to deal with students who come late to class and cheat on their tests. Who can say when and in what way I may go off again?

The patient devoted this session to a discussion of his chance encounter with a young woman he met at a dance in Central Park, New York City, almost 50 years ago. In yet another moment of ungovernable priapism (recall his erection in the middle school Spanish class), the patient unknowingly ejaculated in his pants while dancing with his eroticized partner and the later discovery that his pants were semen-stained caused him acute feelings of mortification.

More problematic, however, were the complications that arose when the fact of the patient's Jewishness, which he had unbendingly hidden from his new girlfriend, was eventually perceived by him to represent an irreconcilable difference between him and this Catholic girl. Professor Kittleman has still not forgiven himself for the cold and heartless way in which he ended their relationship. This particular memory also tellingly reveals two important aspects of the patient's background and personality: first, his inability to be direct and open about his negative emotions, which has caused him to act in ways that are harmful both to himself and others, and, second, his long-standing ambivalence about being a Jew. We have agreed that this latter subject might be a fertile one to further explore in our next session.

It is evident that for the present the patient seeks to use me as a sounding board onto which he may safely pour out his anxieties and frustrations. Clearly, he much prefers me to be a passive listener rather than an active, mutual participant in the therapeutic process. This tendency might in part be attributed to the fact that therapy has just begun and there probably is, on the part of the patient, a sense of urgency "to tell his tale" without being distracted by even intermittent comments from me, no matter how well intended or germane. Also, I must remind myself that he is, after all, a professor of many years standing and perhaps has simply become accustomed to being professorial, or at least pedagogical, in his general demeanor toward others. Or, perhaps more to the point, he is relating in a style that might be considered classic in highly narcissistic personalities; that is, he views and treats me as a self-object whose primary function is to mirror his every need and wish. We shall see.

K: Based on where we ended our last session, I suppose it might be well for me to launch right in and tell you how and why I became a marginalized and equivocal Jew, although I must say at the outset that I have never truly thought of myself as a Jew-hater or anything close to being a Jewish anti-Semite, although some people, including some of my Jewish friends, may disagree, especially when they hear me angrily assail some of Israel's policies and actions toward the Palestinian people.

Leaving politics aside for the moment, I might begin by describing how my parents practiced their faith. The matter of religion or religious teachings was hardly ever discussed in our home. The house we lived in throughout my childhood had an old, rusty, mezuzah nailed to the front doorpost, affixed there, evidently, by an erstwhile Jewish tenant. This mezuzah, more than any of our other household objects, was a daily symbol and reminder of our family's Jewish faith but was put to ritualistic use only by my mother, who each day, upon leaving or returning home, would delicately touch the weather-beaten case with her fingertips and then raise the curled tips of her fingers to her lips to give them a very cursory kiss, as if she was as aware as I that she was carrying myriad germs to her mouth and could safely fulfill this act of piety only as far as the parameters of oral hygiene would allow.

After my grandparents died my mother lit *Yahrzeit* candles to honor and commemorate them on the anniversaries of their deaths. There was a menorah that proudly sat on the top shelf of our dining room cabinet but it was largely forsaken, encrusted with hard stalactites of wax from lightings of many years past. I sometimes wondered if its state of forsakenness made that menorah less a symbol of Hanukah than of the plight of the Jewish people during the Holocaust. Anyway, Dr. Taub, that is about the extent of the religious practices and religiosity that held sway in the Kittleman home. My family did not go to synagogue, not even on high holy days. I did, or sometimes did not go to school on Rosh Hashanah or Yom Kippur, depending upon the whims of my parents. I knew I was Jewish of course. Almost all of my relatives were Jewish (there was one interfaith marriage, generally looked upon askance by the family) and some of them attended synagogue services. All of my parents' friends were Jewish and some of them were very religious. All of this reinforced my sense of being a bona fide Jew, although for some time I must have considered myself mostly a gastronomical one because, although we did not go out to eat very often, whenever we did we usually went to a Jewish restaurant, a deli or a dairy establishment on Prince Street in the old Jewish neighborhood of Newark. I relished the corned beef sandwiches and delicious sour pickles at the delis (right out of the barrel, where they had been aromatically bobbing about moments before) and thought the cheese blintzes I was made to eat at the dairy restaurants were by far an inferior rival for my appetite.

Taking my a-religious upbringing into account, you might imagine, Dr. Taub, how surprised and confused I was when, at the age of 12 and three months, my parents decided to enroll me in a Hebrew school, preparatory to my becoming a Bar Mitzvah. I can assure you that no prior discussion with me had taken place before this decision was made; it was presented to me by my parents as a fait accompli and a salutary one at that.

T: Didn't they explain why they suddenly changed course and decided on religious training for you?

K: No, they did not. But, you know, from what I can recall the decision wasn't explained in religious terms at all. I was merely told that I would attend Hebrew School a few times a week, study the Hebrew language, attend classes on Jewish history and culture and then have a Bar Mitzvah that would make them, me, and all of my close relatives very proud and happy. Contrary to what they thought, the prospect of my suddenly journeying into such a foreign, arcane academic and linguistic territory as Hebrew studies—a realm my worried mind caused me to view as a kind of impenetrable "heart of darkness"—seemed rather ominous to me and I therefore could not understand why my parents believed any of this would make me happy.

T: Jewish parents don't usually wait quite so long before enrolling their kids in Hebrew School. Why did your parents wait so long?

K: That's a question I can answer only with unsatisfactory speculations, Dr. Taub, but I'll do my best. I suppose my parents may have considered the possibility of not having me study to be a Bar Mitzvah at all. Perhaps they had determined to dispense with my religious education entirely. Then one day they wake up, have a nice breakfast of bacon and eggs, and somehow realize that they are answerable to friends, relatives and, if they are at all religious (remember my mother kissing her mezuzah-caressed fingertips), God himself, for their apostasy.

So maybe my enrollment in Hebrew School was just an eleventh hour afterthought, a scampering attempt to stave off the shock and criticism of relatives and the wrath of God, who, after all, had not many years before allowed millions of Jews to die in gas chambers. Who could say what He might yet do to those Jews who flouted and scorned such religious duties as the Bar Mitzvah?

Another, and perhaps better explanation, relates to a chronically serious problem in the Kittleman household during those years: money worries. As a dry cleaner, my father earned very little, even when he owned his own business after many years of working for highly successful and underpaying employers. My father's scant earnings became a nightly bone of contention between him and my mother, which invariably burst into raucous and mean battles royal that might last for hours. For a short time my father had, successively, two partners. The first was addicted to playing poker during the day with his cronies and therefore showed up for work only sporadically. My father bought him out in no time. The second partner was an avowed Communist who denounced capitalism, profit, and private enterprise and tried to convince my father that his eschewal of lucrative daily work was based on his idealistic political philosophy. My father, who had little use for philosophies of any kind, dumped this partner as quickly as he had the first. But, as you might imagine, all of this wrangling and jettisoning of partners cost my father valuable time and considerable money.

In any event, it is quite possible my parents' financial straits forced them to incur the cost of a Hebrew School tuition that spanned the course of only several months rather than years. So they opted for an eight-month enrollment. I also don't know if they applied for and received a tuition-reducing scholarship for me at the Hebrew School. If they did, it was never mentioned.

The term culture shock has enjoyed considerable currency in recent years but that term would have perfectly described my first days at Hebrew School over 50 years ago. I can only guess why my parents decided upon this particular synagogue for my Bar Mitzvah studies. The synagogue was located in a part of the city about two miles from my home, reached in about 20 minutes by the stop-at-each-corner 5 Kinney bus. It had been founded in this once Jewish neighborhood many decades before and had become something of an institutional anachronism in a by-then largely black neighborhood. So perhaps its geographical convenience had something to do with my parents' choice. An oddity to this choice, however, was the fact that this was a Conservative synagogue, which meant that my parents had somehow leapfrogged from a home of non-practicing Judaism (if such an oxymoronic animal exists) to a rather formalistic house of worship without, evidently, entertaining the possibility that a Reformed temple, with its more relaxed religious ceremonies and requirements might have been a less inhospitable and jarring milieu for me.

Before I had even spent one day there, my feelings toward the Hebrew School had become jaundiced by an experience involving my mother. Soon after my father had come home from work, we sat down to dinner. He asked her how her day had gone and she burst into a loud, spasmodic sob. Of course sobbing was not an unheard-of form of emotional expression for my mother but she usually reserved her serious weeping for the battles royal with my father. My father and I were jolted into speechlessness by the depth of her anguish, completely at a loss as to how to assuage it. So we just sat there for what seemed like hours until she slowly gasped her way back to composure. Now we held our breath since almost any cataclysmic event—the death of a mahjong friend, for example—might have caused such an intense outpouring of grief and we didn't know what to expect.

My mother finally found the wherewithal to explain herself. She had visited the synagogue in order to register me for enrollment. As she passed along the mazy halls of the place looking for the registrar's office, she encountered a man striding in her direction. Although she had no idea who he was, his authoritative bearing suggested that he could help find her way to the proper office. My mother, according to her explanation, stopped him with characteristic politeness by saying, "Excuse me, sir, but could you please direct me to where I can register my son for Hebrew School?" The man brusquely pointed down the hall without uttering a word. Sensing she may have given offense by interrupting the man while he was in pursuit of an importunate duty, she thought she might make amends by amicably asking, "Do you work here at the Hebrew School, sir?"

The man turned toward her with an icy and contemptuous frown on his face and said, "Madam, I am Dr. Delman, the rabbi of this synagogue." With that he turned on his heels and martially strode away without saying another word.

Where did this experience leave my mother? To hear her tell it, she had just been through one of the most humiliating experiences of her life. She had insulted the renowned Dr. Delman, a man recognized throughout both the rabbinate and the city of Newark as a great scholar and community leader. Who was she, Doris Kittleman, whose father was a lowly house painter and husband a struggling dry cleaner, to even approach such a man merely to ask for directions to an office? To compound her feelings of debasement, between sobs she repeated over and over again that she had committed a stupid and truly sacrilegious act by not recognizing this godlike man about whom she had heard many awe-inspiring encomia from friends and relatives.

After listening to my mother repeatedly explain to us why the world would be a better place had she never been born, I decided to take the bull by the horns and challenge some of the premises of her self-directed jihad. I may have been only 12 at the time but I already understood something about the nature of incivility and cruelty and decided to console my inconsolable mother with my brilliant insights. I began by saying, "Ma, you've got things upside-down. You weren't rude and disrespectful to the rabbi. He acted like a schmuck toward you. How were you to know who he was? You had never met the man before." Even more perturbed, she replied, "Sheldon, don't use words like that, especially about a rabbi. It isn't nice. And besides, a man like Dr. Delman shouldn't be asked directions by an ordinary person like me. I insulted the man with my ignorance and chutzpah." "Ma, you were lost and needed help. Who's allowed to ask the rabbi directions to the registration office without being rudely snubbed, President Truman? I don't care who he is; he had no right to treat you that way. As a rabbi, he should have known better." She persisted, however, by pointing out that at my age there were some things I simply could not understand and only time would bring me the requisite wisdom to grasp. This bitter bromide parents have used for centuries to one-up and shut up their intelligent, dissentient children served its intended purpose. I gave up, left the dinner table and my parents to settle their own muddled affairs. For several days afterward my mother drooped about the house, dispirited and preoccupied. Gradually, however, the ghost of Count Delman, the sobriquet I used in referring to the rabbi in my private conversations with myself because his diabolical visage, as described by my mother, reminded me of the bloodsucking Bela Lugosi in the Count Dracula movies, ceased to haunt our home.

T: You really took it on the chin when your mother not only didn't agree with your opinion of the rabbi but rebuffed your compassionate attempts to console her.

K: Dr Taub, perhaps you've heard the gag about the Jewish mother who was dismissed from jury duty because she kept insisting that she was the guilty party. My mother, to my knowledge, never served jury duty, but it would not surprise me that if she had been asked to appear for that purpose at the county court house and entered the jury room, the prosecuting attorneys would have taken one whiff of her surfeit of guilt and dismissed her with peremptory challenges rather than lose their case. Yes, there was no dissuading my mother from treading on herself once she picked up steam and had her heart set on attaining martyrdom.

T: We must stop for the day. I'd like, however, to share a thought or two. Your description of the way in which your parents enrolled you in Hebrew School seems to reveal several important things at once: First, it explains why you felt marginalized as a Jew, having had little mooring in the Jewish faith at home before you suddenly received a Jewish education at the Hebrew School. But you've also revealed an important disconnect that existed between your parents and you due to their inability to collaborate and consult with you about decisions that deeply affected your life, such as the decision to enroll you in Hebrew School. This flaw in their parenting was likely to cause you to feel powerless and directionless in deciding your own fate. Finally, your mother's overweening sense of guilt probably had the effect of making you extremely sensitive to her despondent moods and to her seeming fragility. I would suppose that you often felt guilty because you simply could not lift her out of her gloomy moods or dispel her harsh self-judgments.

K: I've always found it hard to gauge how much of my guilt and moodiness was absorbed by me, in some mysterious, osmotic way, from my mother. I'll give it some serious thought, Dr. Taub. See you next week.

Professor Kittleman's Diary 5/27/06

I knew when I opted for psychoanalytic therapy that I would be spending a considerable amount of time rehashing and reliving the past. Now that bitter memories of Hebrew School are vividly in my everyday thoughts, I find it hard to concentrate on my work or recreational reading. Diary, is there something I don't know or have forgotten about this phase of my life that I need to plumb and better understand? Or will I forever meander about in search of the Holy Grail and wind up discovering what I already know—that I was screwed over by loving parents who didn't take the time or have the inclination to sit down with me and explain why religion and a Bar Mitzvah were essential to my future success as a Jewish person in a largely Gentile world.

I haven't yet told Dr. Taub the worst of it. He's touched upon what his theoretical school refers to as serious empathic parental failures during my childhood. As he has no doubt sensed, I sometimes find myself harboring deep resentment over my parents' belated and misguided attempts to rescue my Jewish identity and my very soul by sending me to a house of worship to become a Bar Mitzvah. It remains especially baffling and infuriating to me that not once during my eight-month enrollment in the Hebrew School did they ever consider it necessary to ask me anything about what I thought or felt about my captivity in that sectarian stockade.

Dr. Taub remains sensitively attuned to my feelings of vulnerability and rage. Perhaps some of his kindness and sensitivity will eventually rub off on me and make up for some of my parents' dimwitted ways. Will this then cause me to hate him even more? After all, the more I come to admire and respect his exemplary human qualities and professional skills, the more I seem to envy and despise the man. I recognize that my pain and hatred flow out of a deep, empty cavern of longing for the comforting love and understanding I never received from my poor befuddled parents, but is an increased awareness of this fact going to help me fill the cavern? Is insight enough? I doubt it; Freud's single-minded battle plan to heighten each patient's awareness of his unconscious, often to the exclusion of other considerations such as the attuned understanding and support of the analyst, was only partially successful and has been widely debunked on both theoretical and practical grounds. What, then, is curative or healing about the process of psychotherapy anyway? With Dr. Taub's help, I hope to find out.

As I've pointed out to the patient, his parents' bumbling, autocratic way of enrolling him in Hebrew School left him with profound feelings of vulnerability and emotional impotence. He has not yet related what actually occurred during his enrollment at the school to cause him to use such pejorative terms as "captivity" to describe the experience, but his mother's humiliating encounter with the rabbi of the synagogue during registration certainly must have portended, in the mind of the 12-year-old Sheldon Kittleman, that he was entering, to use his (somewhat hyperbolic) phrase, "the heart of darkness."

The patient continues to use our sessions to advantage. His affect when expressing feelings of sadness or joy is appropriate and he capably describes psychologically relevant events in an organized, spontaneous manner, although the prolixity of his style of speaking suggests that he sometimes uses speech, less for the purpose of communicating information or feelings, than as an attention- and adulation-seeking verbal device. The early-phase transference appears to be largely positive, although I anticipate that a negative transference will soon ascend as the patient begins to attribute to me, transferentially, some of the more distressing characteristics of his parents—e.g., their autocratic tendencies, their gross and blundering inattentiveness to his intimate feelings, and their unwillingness to brook critical dissent from him. A deep analysis of these projections should shed considerable light on Professor Kittleman's intrapsychic and interpersonal conflicts, which, it is hoped, will be of considerable benefit to him.

Fifth Session 6/1/06

K: If it's okay with you, Dr. Taub, I'd like to continue the tale of the eight-month stretch I spent at Gulag Hebrew School.

T: By all means. Go right ahead.

K: Thank you. Well, my very first day there was a chilling eye-opener. As soon as I stepped off the 5 Kinney bus and walked by the synagogue parking lot I knew I was an outlander entering a realm of society to which I would never qualify for membership, except, perhaps, as an outlandish social oddity. The parking lot was filling up with taxis that had driven down from the Weequahic section of the city, a largely Jewish and, by contrast to my neighborhood in the Central Ward, well-to-do part of the city. Boys and girls of my age were spilling out of the cabs in groups of four or five. One cab, I noticed, disgorged seven, who leapt out with the alacrity of circus clowns. At a single glance I was able to comprehend a few salient characteristics of these groups that had a jarring effect upon my senses. First, all of these children seemed to know each other and were in light, happy conversation with one another. Second, and most obvious, they, unlike me, rode in cabs to the Hebrew School. Third, the clothes they wore gave the appearance of being new, very expensive and extremely stylish. One boy, who passed close to me, wore a beautiful fleece-lined parka with a soft fur collar and hood that, from all appearances, could brave the bitterest New Jersey winters.

Being bombarded by strong adverse impressions, I remember feeling that I wanted to run back to the bus stop, hop a 5 Kinney and return home before any of those children discovered that I was to be one of their classmates.

T: What, specifically, set you apart from them? What upset you so much that you thought you might have to decamp so quickly?

K: Let's start with the cabs, Dr. Taub. At the time I was 12 and had never ridden in a cab. My father owned a car, an old jalopy, which tootled us around town and even to the suburbs, the South Orange "mountains," where the air was cooler during the summer months than in the muggy city streets. But in my mind, people who rode in cabs belonged to a privileged caste that outranked my family and all the people who lived in my neighborhood by a long shot. Now that I think of it, I do remember a cab once picking up one of our neighbors in order to rush her to the hospital to have a baby, but cabs in our neighborhood were almost as scarce as bison. Anytime my friends and I had to go anywhere on our own that was not within reasonable walking distance, we took a bus. So, when I saw these kids getting out of cabs at the synagogue, I at once saw myself as an outcast in their midst. I know, Dr. Taub, you may be thinking that I greatly exaggerated my plight since those kids probably came from a greater distance than I (they did), and therefore needed faster transportation to the synagogue in order to arrive there on time. It might be argued, therefore, that their riding in cabs reflected a practical necessity, not a class distinction. As well, since four, five, or even seven kids shared a cab, the fare per kid was probably not much more expensive than my bus fare.

Those are logical observations. But at the time I was a callow 12-year-old desperately searching for signs and initiatives of chumminess—a glancing smile, a friendly wave of the hand, a minimal verbal gesture like "Hi, what's your name?"; in other words, any hint of affinity or welcome from this bevy of seemingly carefree and vivacious youngsters with whom I was to attend Hebrew School for almost a year. Instead I received from them icy exclusion, incuriosity, condescension, and nullification in the form of cold-shouldering rebuffs whenever I attempted to be the least bit friendly.

I mentioned, Dr. Taub, the matter of dress wear. My clothes were not exactly threadbare but were identifiably shabby hand-me-downs that had been worn first by older cousins and even uncles. By the time they outfitted me they were not only absurdly unfashionable but rarely matched my size. Thus, my pants and shirts were, more often than not, either too baggy or too tight. Some of the clothes I wore were also unwittingly donated to me by my father's customers, who either completely forgot to retrieve them from his dry cleaning establishment after several years or moved away before redeeming them. I suppose my father didn't consider this to be a form of stealing since the clothes were evidently not important or valuable enough for these customers to even remember leaving them with him. I recall being particularly embarrassed whenever I had pocketed a customer's handkerchief before leaving home and then plucked it out in the middle of a sneeze, only to discover, along with at least one of my Hebrew School classmates, that the brightly emblazoned monogram on the handkerchief did not match either my forename or surname.

T: Are you then suggesting that part of the ostracism you encountered at the Hebrew School was generated by the clothes you wore?

K: Definitely. No doubt about it. My clothes drew many a jaundiced stare from classmates and I can assure you, Dr. Taub, the daily once-overs I got from them could be quite wilting.

T: Did things get better or worse after that first day?

K: I can best answer that question by telling you that many years afterward I told my father that if he had intended and planned for me to become an unregenerate atheist, he could not have done a better job than by enrolling me in that Hebrew School. The classroom teacher was, admittedly, a friendly, quiet, prepossessing man who seemed to accept my anomalous presence in his class. Since I read well, I completed homework assignments in a timely and competent manner. We studied biblical and modern Jewish history, which included many prideful teacher-led discussions about the recent establishment of the State of Israel. I recall a solicitation was made to parents for contributions in support of Israel for which each student would receive the distinction of having an honorific tree planted in that country in his or her name. I suppose "my" tree may still be growing somewhere in that strife-torn land if it hasn't been bulldozed or blown up by now.

Studying and learning the Hebrew language was a different matter, however. The other students were rather conversant with the language having already spent several years learning it at the Hebrew School. Because I simply could not adequately accelerate my grasp of Hebrew in that class of advanced students to even remotely approach parity with them, I was sent to a tutor. Mr. White, the tutor, was a stiff, formal, and sanctimonious young man who bore in my young imagination a startling and lamentable resemblance to Ichabod Crane, whom I had met in the *Legend of Sleepy Hollow* the previous year. Each week Mr. White and I squeezed into a cramped, steamy room where I was to learn the Hebrew alphabet by copying it into lined blue books (identical to those I later used in my college examinations) and then reading complete words from a text with proper pronunciation. The odd, hieroglyphic shapes of the Hebrew letters with their tees, dots and colons reposing beneath them at first defied my understanding. But gradually I got the hang of it and began to mechanically mumble my way through these tutorials well enough to ward off some of Ichabod's worst jeremiads.

My best day, by far, was my last with this loathsome man. A cold front had ushered in below-freezing temperatures in the Northeast but inside the well-heated Hebrew School the rooms were warm and cozy. About midway through our lesson the radiator that was located right behind me and had been working overtime to keep up with the arctic winds that were buffeting the window, began to whistle in a high-pitched, sibilant manner. Mr. White, who was reading with his back to me, turned around each time the whistling noise signaled the effluence of steam. After a while he paid it no more attention. As I sat there scribing away at my lesson, I realized that this was my last day with Mr. White and I had not yet done anything to overtly indicate my profound hatred for him. In a small room shared by just the two of us almost any act of insubordination on my part was easily detectable and therefore punishable. Again I heard the sound of the radiator whistling. When it stopped I emitted through my lower front teeth a thin teakettle whistle without visibly moving my lips that was indistinguishable from the radiator's. The mimicry was so good that Mr. White at first took no notice of it. When the radiator resumed its whistling, I ceased my own.

For many minutes the radiator and I alternated our one-note sonata. Mr. White was by now listening to an unbroken skein of whistling that must have become exasperating because he suddenly spun around and angrily stared at the false culprit, the radiator. When he did, I stop whistling and a strange silence filled the room. Mr. White then stared at me malevolently, searching my face for a telltale sign of culpability, but I gave him none. I kept my head down and continued writing cherubically. With a bit of a snort he turned around and resumed his reading and when he did I resumed my whistling. I tweaked Mr. White with this cat-and-mouse game many times but not once did he catch me at my deviltry and when our last session was finally over he wished me well with a frigidity matching that of the nor'easter that was squalling outside our window.

I suppose I can safely say that the grand apotheosis of my Hebrew School days was not my Bar Mitzvah but the day my regular teacher was absent due to illness. His last-minute replacement was Mr. Fox, a doddering, befuddled septuagenarian who served as the shammas (kind of handyman) of the synagogue and on this day also served as an ad hoc teacher. His specialty, I observed, was in passing out talitim and yarmulkes for the synagogue services. Perhaps, on this particular day someone mistook him for a shaman rather than a shammas, believing he could use his magical powers to inspire or at least control fidgety students like myself. But Mr. Fox seemed not to care about the day's assignments, so he laxly drifted in and out of the classroom, leaving the students to fend for themselves.

By happenstance, on that day one of the boys smuggled into the classroom a large, multicolored block of clay. Soon after Mr. Fox made one of his escapes into the hallway, the smuggler dismembered the clay block into little pieces which he quickly and stealthily distributed to all the other boys. I somehow managed to garner a rather large chunk for myself and suddenly tiny clay pellets were soaring, pell-mell, about the room and ricocheting off walls and windows. Without conscious forethought or plan, I suppose, all the boys hurried to battle stations along the far wall where they aligned themselves into a brigade to engage me in a frenzied but entirely bloodless battle. I assumed my position against the opposite wall where I faced them entirely alone. The girls in the class scurried to the front of the room in order to get out of the way of the flying clay-missiles. One of them, evidently very frightened by this sudden outbreak of mass lunacy, ran off to find Mr. Fox.

The epic clay-war lasted no more than five minutes. But, as I have already said, those five minutes were the apotheosis of my Hebrew School career. All the pent-up resentment and fury I had felt day after day in those oppressive surroundings erupted in that harmless free-for-all. For a full 300 seconds I was Judas Maccabaeus heroically fighting my own war of liberation.

I threw clay as hard and as accurately as I could at the heads of my enemies. Ducking and hopping about, I took very few of their projectiles squarely on the head. When I did get hit, however, a triumphant cheer went up from the other side of the room. When Mr. Fox reentered the classroom, he shouted angrily for an immediate cease-fire. We spent the rest of the afternoon cleaning up the mess we had made and acting penitently for the benefit of Mr. Fox, who was certain to report our misbehavior to our teacher the next day. My concerns, however, were more otherworldly. I had just committed an irreverent and vengeful act in the house of God. As far back as I could remember, I had always doubted the existence of God, but never so completely that I could feel entirely safe from his wrath, should He perchance exist. Following the clay-war, I continued to despise my classmates and the Hebrew School, but I behaved with greater circumspection while in the synagogue itself, just in case there really was a God and I was perhaps in His dog house.

T: You must have recited and sung prayers during synagogue services. What effect did that have upon your feelings of religiosity or, if you prefer, irreligiosity?

K: First of all, I learned Hebrew entirely by rote; consequently, I had no idea what any of the words meant. When I mouthed them during services, my mind was elsewhere, mostly on playing with my friends when I got home. To amuse and distract myself, I sometimes inserted, sotto voce, curse words into the prayers I recited or sang. I must confess, however, that some of the music that accompanied the prayers was very melodic and, since I had a decent singing voice, I didn't mind joining in the singing of the prayers with the other kids. But I never once had what might be called a pious or transcendental moment of spiritual devotion or elevation during any of the services and wondered how all of these demonstrably intelligent children could be so damnably credulous. Dr. Taub, I do recall, however, how my intransigent posture of disbelief and iconoclasm recurrently caused me to feel an admixture of strange, contradictory emotions, a kind of abject defectiveness alternating with a princely inimitability.

As the time of my Bar Mitzvah drew near, I was required to receive my preparatory lessons from Cantor Baum, in his home in Hillside, a town south of and contiguous with Newark. Each Sunday morning for over a month I took the 3 Bergen bus to the cantor's Hillside home where he instructed me in my Bar Mitzvah readings. I had never met the cantor before, although I had observed him each week as he led the singing during Sabbath services. He was a large, burly man with a deep, resonant voice that amply filled the capacious synagogue. Although his manner as he stood at the bema each week seemed haughty and self-aggrandizing, I did not at first dread or resist these Sunday-morning lessons, even though they cut deeply into my weekend playtime.

As it turned out, the cantor was a perfectionist and a despot. As I recited my lessons, he glowered at me, seemingly relishing his every chance to correct a mispronounced or misread word. Since I was not a proficient reader in Hebrew (I was in English), and was quite nervous under the cantor's hawkeyed scrutiny, I made many mistakes. Like a voracious predator, he pounced upon each one with unbridled sarcasm and belligerence.

"Can't you get it into your thick head, that that word is not pronounced that way? Idiot, you just skipped a word. You expect to get Bar Mitzvahed with such a stupid brain as yours? A fine Jewish boy you are. You are a disgrace to your parents and your faith. Now, pronounce this word correctly, dummy."

The cantor leveled these and other abuses at me from very close range and in a stentorian voice. His face became livid and contorted with rage as he took obvious sadistic pleasure in terrifying and degrading me. It was often a great sweaty struggle for me to withstand his savage onslaughts without feeling that I was about to melt into uncontrollable sobbing at any moment. His merciless, cold stares, the fixity of his baleful, imperious demeanor, and his full-throated, bellowing and captious voice, saturated my very being with fear and blinding hatred for the man. But I was able to persevere by blinking back my tears and imagining myself somewhere, anywhere, else. My vivid imagination, which housed some very vicious, vengeful thoughts toward the brutish cantor, enabled me to weather my tutorial sessions, but serious emotional wounds had been inflicted and went largely untreated.

One day, after a particularly stormy session, I strolled slowly and disconsolately up a hilly street toward the bus stop, wishing with all my heart that I would never have to return to the cantor's insufferable home again. Suddenly, I heard a loud, thunderous noise that seemed to come from some distant place in the stratosphere. I stopped walking and looked up, expecting to see a storm cloud, but the sky was infinitely cloudless and devoid of menace. The distant boom continued for several seconds, but since it had no visible meteorologic provenance, I quickly gave up trying to explain it to myself. (I learned from a scarehead in the next day's newspaper that the sound had come from a large oil refinery that had exploded in the "down-neck" section of Newark, causing extensive devastation.)

Looking down from the sky, I realized that the place where I was standing on the sidewalk was covered with a large army of marching, single-minded reddish ants. The ants were traversing the sidewalk in thin, straight lines, carrying food particles on their backs into the narrow dirt-chinks of the cement. There was a driven and relentless aspect to the ants' behavior, which immediately revolted and infuriated me. The blind conformity and methodicalness with which they carried out their mindless tasks seemed to mirror and mock my own dreary existence. I thought fleetingly of the cantor, whom I had left only a few minutes before. I then began to step upon the ants.

The ants, seeing some of their comrades go down, broke ranks and began to race madly and helplessly in all directions. I went after them, crushing 15 or 20 at a time beneath the soles and heels of my shoes. I was determined that none would escape my hecatomb. A small number did find their way into the earth, but in less than 10 minutes I had destroyed perhaps over a thousand of them. The sidewalk was bleached with their blood and, when I left the site, there was no sign of life, where only minutes before there had been a vibrant, flourishing ant migration. I rode the bus home that day realizing that I had just committed a heinous form of mass murder. To make matters worse, I understood nothing of what had inspired me to carry out such a genocidal act of vengeance. I knew, even then, that I could never entirely forgive myself for what I had done to those defenseless and inculpable ants.

My Bar Mitzvah went off quite flawlessly. I gained considerable confidence as I proceeded through with my Torah readings and even possessed sufficient cockiness to flash an occasional smile at my Gentile friends who sat in the audience looking quite ill at ease and comical in their yarmulkes and tallitim. At the conclusion of the service, my friend Mike crowned my success by remarking, with great sincerity and generosity, that I had conducted myself throughout the ceremonies with an impressive grown-upness that he had never before seen in me.

Immediately following the services, I was assailed by strange and unexpected feelings of incompleteness. The cantor was very much on my mind. Although I had every reason to feel joyous and pleased with myself, I realized that I had continued to hate him and that my hatred for him was ruining my celebration of the Bar Mitzvah. I looked among the gathering of well-wishers for the cantor, but he had already left the immediate area. I thought he might have retired to a nearby anteroom, so I knocked at the door of the room. A deep and painfully familiar voice advised me to enter. Cantor Baum was standing near a bookcase where he was perusing one of the texts.

"What is it, Sheldon?"

"Cantor Baum."

"Yes, well, what is it?" he asked impatiently.

"Cantor Baum, I wanted to say…" I didn't know what I had wanted to say.

"Sheldon, you wanted to say what?" the cantor queried with increasing severity.

"Cantor Baum, I wanted to thank you for helping me with my Bar Mitzvah lessons and I, I, uh, wanted to tell you that, that, I think you're a…very nice man."

The cantor look quizzically at me for a moment and then an expression formed on his face that was entirely unfamiliar to me. With an almost beatific smile, he came over to me, patted me on the head, and said, "Nice work today, Sheldon. You did well. Mazel Tov." He believed my lie and was congratulating me. I also, by the way, believed my lie. The cantor was most assuredly not a nice man, but, for some inexplicable reason, I could not consummate my Bar Mitzvah, my ritual passage into Jewish adulthood, without childishly renouncing my hatred for him.

Family and friends later gathered at Tunis Mansion on Bergen Street for the post-Bar Mitzvah celebration. My parents basked in the extravagant compliments and blessings they received on my behalf. As expected, the Bar Mitzvah boy and his family were toasted roundly. The cantor also gave a toast. He rose slowly and pompously to his feet and looked out upon his auditors with smarmy self-assurance.

He said, "I, too, ladies and gentlemen, wish to give a toast on this joyous occasion to Sheldon and his proud parents. But, I also wish to tell a little story, a story about something that happened just today. I was in one of the offices after the end of services. I heard a knock at my door and, when it opened, Sheldon entered. I asked why he had come. He said it was to let me know that he thought I was a nice man and he wanted to thank me for the help I had given him. I want you all to know of Sheldon's fine gesture. Mazel Tov, Sheldon. Mazel Tov, Mr. and Mrs. Kittleman."

At the end of the cantor's toast everyone showered approving smiles and applause upon me for the lie I had told. My hatred for the man had been revived and intensified manifold by his self-serving speech. Unlike the others, I knew full well that he was using the opportunity primarily to celebrate himself and perhaps, more importantly, to also exonerate himself from his atrocious treatment of me in his home. I shunned him throughout the remainder of the celebration and never again exchanged

Professor Kittleman's Therapy

another word with him, although I did run across him many times in later years.

T: Our time is about up. Based on your description of your Hebrew School experience, I can certainly understand why you turned away from religion. What also seems clear and important is the enormous guilt that compelled you to thank the cantor for his help when you obviously wanted to denounce him instead. He certainly gave you good reason to despise him but your guilt over hating him so much caused you to verbally forgive him. I use the word "verbally" because it's clear, to me at least, that you have never truly forgiven him.

K: You're absolutely right about the fact that I've never forgiven him. And I suppose when I wanted to kill him and killed the ants instead, I found it hard to forgive myself for unleashing my fury on them. I know I also found it difficult to forgive myself for my display of cowardice toward the cantor, thanking him when I should have flayed him for the emotional torture he put me through. But I was just a kid and couldn't find the words, or more importantly, the courage to do that. Perhaps next time, if you don't mind, I'd like to tell you my thoughts about forgiveness. It's a matter to which I've given considerable thought.

T: If you'd like. Take care.

K: Dr. Taub?

T: Yes?

K: In one of his novels Balzac opines that suffering predisposes the mind to devoutness. Unfortunately, Balzac did not have me in mind when he wrote what he thought was a truism. The suffering I endured at the Hebrew School predisposed me to irreverence, impiety and atheism and for that, perhaps, I should be grateful (if I am not, by saying so, greedily searching for a silver lining among some very shoddy rags). See you next time.

Professor Kittleman's Diary 6/4/06

Diary, this session was a visceral doozy. Dredging up memories of the privileged kids in my Hebrew School class, my contemptuous (and contemptible) tutor, Mr. Ichabod White, and the despotic Cantor Baum, the rank sadist who caused me to commit entomological mass murder, left me an emotional dishrag after this session. I hated them all, in varying degrees of course, and reliving my worst moments with them in the Hebrew School has left in its wake feelings of raw fury. I've also noticed, not surprisingly, that my murderous ideations toward Dr. Taub were given a nice fillip by these vivid recollections. Yes, diary, I know transference feelings toward a therapist, either hostile or positive, do not necessarily originate with mental images and memories of one's parents; which explains why a revivification of a long-dead, child-abusing cantor can conjure up a quite juicy mental vendetta for a blameless therapist.

The patient described a series of adverse and traumatizing experiences when attending Hebrew School for approximately eight months, preparatory to becoming a Bar Mitzvah. The fact that he was, compared to his classmates, at a decided disadvantage, socially and academically, deprived him of feelings of belonging and entitlement. To make matters worse, he was tutored by a man who relied upon strict and exacting pedagogical methods that served to fuel the patient's resentment for him. Worst of all, the patient was required to undergo Bar Mitzvah lessons with an overbearing and vitriolic cantor whose repeated verbal pummeling caused the patient murderous hatred that was displaced onto a defenseless army of ants and then transformed into a reaction formation when he complimented and thanked, rather than vilified, the cantor for the way in which he had been treated by him. It will be interesting and worthwhile to note if and how the patient continues to use these particular defense mechanisms when he becomes angry with others now, especially here in the therapy.

K: I mentioned toward the end of our last session that I wanted to discuss the matter of forgiveness. Do you mind if I just go ahead?

T: Please.

K: I attach great emotional significance to the matter of forgiveness and I think I know some of the reasons why. My mother rarely spoke ill of a person. In this country, and in this time, behavior of this type is usually viewed as virtuous. But is it, necessarily? Even though my mother did not say nasty things or viciously gossip about other people, that does not mean that she did not, from time to time, harbor vile thoughts about them. As I often observed as a child, my mother would be on the verge of saying something cruel or ugly about someone and then catch herself, bite her tongue, figuratively speaking, and swallow her words. From the pinched and irresolute expression on her face, I could tell that she was about to fulminate over someone she had seen stealing a grapefruit at the local grocery store, or telling a dirty joke in mixed company, or making an anti-Semitic remark on the bus within earshot of her seat. Instead, the first words of complaint would almost inaudibly dribble out and then be inhaled in a single breath, as if truncated at their root. She simply could not permit herself to utter a full, declarative denunciation of even egregious individuals who had committed crimes and other dishonorable acts.

Was she, in doing so, acting virtuously? At the risk of appearing uncharitable, I doubt it. I believe she was, at bottom, deathly afraid of offending God or violating the dicta of her strict, censorious and very dead parents, or some other awful powers that inhabited the imagination of her psyche by saying something for which she believed she would be severely punished or even struck dead.

T: Can you give me an example of how she manifested this fear in her everyday relationships?

K: Easily. My mother had an older sister with whom she was symbiotically close from early childhood on. There's a 90-year-old photograph I have of my mother and her sister sitting next to each other on a sofa.

This photograph shows my mother leaning against her sister at such an obtuse angle that she is practically in her lap. That photograph is, in my view, a microcosm of their lifelong relationship. My mother could hardly take a pee without first checking with my Aunt Sarah. They were on the phone at least seven times a day and when they weren't on the phone they were visiting each other practically every evening.

Now, Aunt Sarah had a husband who was generally considered to be a hail-fellow-well-met type of guy because of his funny sense of humor; Uncle Bernie was a farceur who could put people in stitches with his jokes and caricatures of goofy relatives and, to boot, was willing to drive great distances to visit and chat amiably with relatives, and even talk politics intelligently because he spent many afternoons viewing the latest news at the Newsreel Theater on Broad Street in Newark. All in all, Uncle Bernie was a pretty good guy. But he had one serious flaw in his character that drove a wedge between the two of us: his insatiable need to needle and belittle my mother. Whenever the two sisters and their husbands got together Uncle Bernie would sit quietly for a while, then an impish smirk would cross his face, and you just knew that he was preparing to ambuscade my mother. Uncle Bernie knew all my mother's vulnerabilities and possessed an uncanny, almost military genius for discerning the weakest points of her highly invadable fortress of selfhood. Most of his jibes were cutting and crude. "Where'd you get that dress, Doris, at the Salvation Army? I think you could do without that dessert, Doris, you're showing quite a midriff there. Doris, can you get me a drink and hurry it up, I'm thirsty." And my mother, Uncle Bernie's ever-dutiful odalisque, would fetch him a drink, and in a hurry. "Oh, thanks, Doris, but what took you so long?" he would say. Sadly, my father did nothing to discourage or interdict these insults and my mother, red-faced from embarrassment, quiescently absorbed them like a sponge. And this verbal travesty went on day after day, with Uncle Bernie slicing up my mother with glee and impunity.

T: What about you? How did you deal with Uncle Bernie's taunting your mother that way?

K: Like my father, I said and did nothing. I simply sat there aboil with rage, plotting imaginary acts of revenge. But by the time I was 15 or 16 I decided to have a heart-to-heart talk with my mother about Uncle

Bernie's abusive behavior. By that time I was a reasonably mature and credible youngster in my mother's eyes, so she was beginning to take my opinions on a wide variety of subjects rather seriously.

I told my mother that Uncle Bernie's sarcasms and ridicule would have to stop, now. I said, "The man is a misogynist who targets women, especially you, Mom, with the worst kind of ugly disparagement. Mom, you have to tell this guy to cut that shit out. It hurts your feelings and, to tell you the truth, it hurts my feelings to watch you being degraded like that day after day. It has got to stop." "Sheldon," she said, "You don't understand. He's my sister's husband. I can't do anything to hurt her, like telling off her husband. Or, God forbid, kicking him out of my house." "Mom, look, try to understand what you're saying. You're telling me that you're willing to tolerate abuse from a schmuck like Uncle Bernie in order to keep your sister happy. Do you think it makes your sister happy to see you miserable? Does it make Dad happy? Does it make me happy? Mom, you've got to stop this bully." With a sigh of heavy sadness and resignation, she said, "I'm sorry, Sheldon, I can't." "Okay, Mom," I replied, "if you won't do it, I will. The next time Uncle Bernie comes here and fires off one of his barbs at you, I'm going to jump on his ass. I'm going to tell him that if he says any more nasty things to you he will not be permitted in our house. That's it, I've had it with him." "Sheldon, you mustn't do that." I think my mother thought I was bluffing since I was normally a very non-confrontational kind of guy, but I wasn't bluffing.

That evening, Aunt Sarah and Uncle Bernie came for dinner. Uncle Bernie kibitzed and bantered with my father through most of the meal. Then, as my mother placed an apple pie a la mode in front of Uncle Bernie, he quipped with a chuckle, "Doris, let me do you a favor and eat your dessert too. Remember what I said about your oversized midriff." With that remark, my mother looked at me with alarm. She saw me bristle with rage and open my mouth in readiness for retaliation. In a flash, she leaped into the fray. "Bernie," she said, "I've had with you. You may think you're funny when you ridicule me, but you're anything but funny. As a matter of fact, you're quite disgusting. Until you find some way to treat me with the respect I deserve, I don't want you in my home. Now get out."

I could not believe my ears. For the first time in my life I heard Mom stand up for herself. And with a forthrightness, pluck, and composure that truly amazed my Aunt Sarah, my father, and me. And most of all, of course, my electrified Uncle Bernie, who sat in his chair with such a dumfounded, demented expression on his face that one might have thought that he had just taken a hammer blow to the head, which, I suppose, he had. Perhaps he was playacting to buy time in order to come up with a jocular riposte that would neutralize my mother's courage and momentum, but I don't think so. He sat there completely immobilized and silent for many minutes. My aunt and my father merely sat there with glum faces and said nothing, but I raised myself in my chair and proudly smiled at my mother, my accomplished protégée. No, that's not fair. My prodding probably helped her find the words, but clearly the momentous dressing down that Uncle Bernie received from my mother was her own masterful breakthrough, her sublime tour de force, for which she deserved full credit. I could well imagine how much cruelty she had had to put up with her entire life from chauvinistic assholes like Uncle Bernie. Somewhere within the depths of her being there must have been a huge stockpile of explosive bitterness over how she had been tormented and trifled with by men like my uncle and now, at long last, she gave him his overdue comeuppance.

T: What did Uncle Bernie do? Did he leave?

K: Sorry, I forgot to finish story. No, Bernie did not leave, at least not right away. He continued to sit there as if he believed his state of dumb lifelessness would bestir my mother to change her mind. But she did not change her mind and she did not take her eyes off him. She watched him in a steadfast, glowering way as if she knew that he might at any moment use some form of opportunistic chicanery to outwit and prevail over her. But my mother was not to be outwitted. When she realized that Uncle Bernie was not going to leave of his own accord, she repeated, this time with bulldoggish ferocity, her earlier command: "Bernie, get out."

Bernie looked, in my eyes, liked a pathetic spanked child. With tears in his eyes and contrition in his tottery gestures, he stood up, grabbed his jacket and, without another word, left the house with Aunt Sarah in his train.

T: Your mother gained a great victory.

K: A Pyrrhic victory, Dr. Taub.

T: What do you mean?

K: What I mean is: no sooner did my aunt and uncle get home, the phone rang. It was Aunt Sarah, blubbering, spilling out apologies to my mother for her husband's repeated acts of abusiveness. Then Aunt Sarah switched tacks by telling my mother (who later repeated this conversation to me) that Uncle Bernie, as soon as they got home, promised to reform. He would no longer mistreat my mother and was willing to apologize himself for hurting her feelings so. My mother, who seemed to sense and appreciate her ascendancy in this domestic melodrama, held fast to her decision to bar Uncle Bernie from our home and told her sister this, time after time. When Aunt Sarah discovered that tacks one and two were not working, she yanked out of her bag of clever tricks a third stratagem that had greater efficacy. She told my mother that living with Uncle Bernie was a life of unremitting misery and that the only thing that lightened her doldrums was her visits with her sister and brother-in-law. And, if my mother didn't buy into this sororal blackmail and permit her and Uncle Bernie visitation privileges, Aunt Sarah would, she intimated, suffer an emotional breakdown, or worse, commit suicide.

Well, what could be worse than being your own beloved sister's murderess? This telephone conversation was repeated, almost word for word, for about two weeks, until my mother weakened and relented under the barrage of Aunt Sarah's hysterical cackling. Uncle Bernie was permitted to resume his visits. His first visit had a kind of *Ozzie and Harriet* normalcy about it. Bernie sat quietly and politely in our living room and when my mother served him tea and freshly baked cookies, he thanked her profusely and complimented each morsel with exaggerated effusions of gastronomic ecstasy. My mother was pleased but not hornswoggled. She maintained a friendly but wary distance from Uncle Bernie, giving him the benefit of her acute doubts. Uncle Bernie bided his time in our house and after a tacit three-week truce between the two antagonists, he reverted to form; that is, he began taunting my mother all over again. I again prodded and coached my mother to fight back, but my incessant carping at her only made her more intransigently defiant toward me, and even more passively compliant toward Uncle Bernie. I finally gave up in disgust.

T: How did she justify the turnaround in her behavior?

K: In two ways. She said that it was necessary for her to support her sister in any way possible, including placing herself on the sacrificial altar of my uncle's abuse. She proclaimed that her forbearance protected my aunt's marriage from strife and even divorce. In other words, in some crazy, see-saw manner, the more the formidable Uncle Bernie was permitted to tromp on my mother, the more humanely he was inclined to treat his wife. Since I myself had seen this imbecilic domestic soap opera reenacted many times before my very own eyes, I did not doubt my mother's contention that she was, through her meek obeisance to my uncle, saving her sister's marriage. That being the case, only one crucial question remained: in light of the debasing humiliations my mother had to go through time after time to save her sister's marriage, was such a personal sacrifice really worth it? I posed this question to my mother and she replied in an uncharacteristically minatory tone that it was most certainly worth it—after all, this was her venerable sister we were discussing—and if I didn't think so, I had better keep my offensive opinions about the matter to myself. My mother had sounded the depths of her conscience and pronounced her edict with an air of triumphant and indisputable finality. That admonition brought closure to my military campaign to neutralize Uncle Bernie's onslaughts and he went on to have many more wonderfully entertaining evenings in our home, tormenting my mother with complete impunity.

T: You said there were two ways your mother justified her turnaround toward Uncle Bernie. What was the second?

K: Oh, yes, sorry. Let me explain the second. I began the session by mentioning that I wanted to discuss the matter of forgiveness and now I see our time is almost up. So I will table that subject for next time. The second way my mother explained her turnaround was this. She said that, no matter how galling Uncle Bernie's behavior had been, the man, at bottom, really meant well. When I heard my mother euphemize and rationalize Uncle Bernie's malevolent motives with such absurd empty-headedness, I saw red and wanted to do what my black friends in the neighborhood talked of doing all the time to people who heedlessly crossed them: hit her upside the head; knock some sense into her. The idea that a man of

Uncle's Bernie's character, the prince of darkness in our home, could actually mean well when he was ripping her, was more than I could bear. I had witnessed my mother's tendency to attribute altruistic motives to evil-minded people throughout my childhood, and it has profoundly shaped the way in which I think about the matter of forgiveness. I hope you'll allow me to elaborate on this subject in our next session.

T: Of course. See you next time.

Diary, this rummaging through the past is a painful business. Since my last session, the revenant of my long-dead Uncle Bernie has appeared in several of my nocturnal dreams, always with that sneering, supercilious expression on his face for which he gained notoriety in our home. He never says anything, but I can tell from the cartoonish sneer on his dream face that he knows he had bested me, mano a mano, in our gladiatorial battle to find the heartland of my mother's dignity; he, for the purpose of ravaging, despoiling, and destroying it, I, for the purpose of cultivating it like a delicate and beautiful flower. Diary, who won? I would have to say it was Uncle Bernie, but perhaps my mother would disagree and, after all, isn't she the only rightful arbiter who can satisfactorily solve this enigma? But, diary, she has not yet appeared in my dreams with the answer.

Dr. Taub's Anamnesis 6/9/06

The patient experienced during adolescence his mother's rather masochistic acquiescence to her brother-in-law's cruelty toward her. Her willingness to sacrifice her dignity and well-being in order to safeguard her sister's marriage bespeaks, it seems, a low level of self-esteem, perhaps accompanied by at least moderate depression. In any case, his mother's incapacity to look out for her rights and welfare induced in the patient feelings of helplessness, resignation, and ineffectuality, remnants of which are still strongly embedded in his character and his current emotional life. The contest between the patient and his "evil-minded" Uncle Bernie for his mother's mind and heart smacks of thwarted Oedipal strivings on the part of the patient that most likely engendered a sense of being a rejected suitor for her love. How much his bitterness over his thwarted, unrequited feelings of love for his mother during adolescence have been generalized within his character structure and his current emotional life remains to be seen.

K: Well, I promised to take up the matter of forgiveness in this session, unless, of course, you would like to ask me something or prefer that I speak on another, perhaps more relevant, topic.

T: No, go right ahead with what you were about to say.

K: Thank you. In order to give you a thumbnail sketch of my thoughts on the subject of forgiveness, Dr. Taub, I probably should start by cheerfully debunking an oft-quoted, widely celebrated aphorism composed by Alexander Pope: "To err is human, to forgive divine." When I first came across those sublime words in a high school anthology, I thought them, well, sublime. I now think them ignorant, naïve, pretentious, and violative of the human spirit and, perhaps worst of all, downright impractical.

T: You don't believe in forgiveness, Professor Kittleman?

K: Oh, I do, Dr. Taub, I do. I would never suggest that this loftiest of human emotions does not exist. That is not my point at all.

T: Then what is your point, Professor Kittleman?

K: Well, I have several points, really. First, forgiveness is not always necessary or humanly possible. Furthermore, the mere effort, sometimes of superhuman proportions, to forgive other persons their transgressions is often quite detrimental to the forgiveness-giver.

T: I don't think I understand. Could you be more specific, Professor Kittleman? Perhaps a few examples would help.

K: Gladly. Let's take the example of rape victims. Many women have been raped since early childhood. Their predators have been their fathers, stepfathers, older brothers, uncles, cousins, their fathers' drinking buddies, their mothers' lovers, strange men on darkened streets, their "quid pro quo" bosses, their teachers, their priests and rabbis, and, let us not forget, their dashing college dates who use the upstairs rooms of frat houses for the perpetration of train rapes, so-named for the sequential, boxcar nature of the crime. Many, if not most of these men, are sociopaths, who lack the capacity for ordinary empathy and compassion. They are guided by an amoral compass that directs them toward sating their gonadal passions as they please, where they please, and when they please, providing, of course, there is no one around to catch them and have them arrested and prosecuted. So, should these baleful men be forgiven by their victims?

T: I take it that you believe they should not be.

K: No, that is not what I am saying. My point is that I don't believe it is my right, or anyone else's right for that matter, to tell these women they should or should not forgive their perpetrators. Many of them feel an inexhaustible hatred toward their predators. What, then, is the psychological or moral value of preaching the necessity of forgiveness to women who already irrationally feel guilty for being raped in the first place and then hate themselves even more for hating a despicable rapist, as strange as that may seem to some people?

T: So, you believe they should not be encouraged to forgive these men by telling them that the perpetrators are troubled individuals who simply can't control their waywardness and therefore need understanding and rehabilitation services, which after all, are forms of forgiveness.

K: Of course I believe these men should be helped; I champion rehabilitative services for sexual offenders—and other troubled people—far more than the average citizen. But that is not my point. I am simply saying that there is nothing intrinsically wrong with hating another person who has traumatized you, from either a psychological or moral point of view.

T: You don't believe that hatred can be all-consuming or dangerous for the person who lugs those hateful feelings about day after day?

K: I think it is not only possible, but abundantly obvious that many people who are consumed with anger lose control of their emotions in violent and dangerous ways—each day the newspapers sensationalize the mayhem they commit. But let us think more circumspectly about this issue. Millions of people in our society are, to use your term for it, lugging about anger of prodigious proportions, most of which is well, if not overly, controlled and is certainly not especially dangerous in any particular way. How is the anger manifested or, as Freud might put it, sublimated? In a myriad of interesting ways.

T: For example?

K: For starters, let's take gossip. Perhaps gossip may be artificially divided under the rubrics of benign or malicious, but everyone knows that gossip is primarily inspired and undergirded by the wish to garner personal information from other individuals—even individuals we love and care about—that can be used to taint them in the eyes of others when the gossips move on to their next conversation with a receptive ear. This form of pleasurably malicious one-upmanship has trumped baseball as America's number one pastime. It is engaged in over the phone, over the dinner table, over the conference table at work, and, most certainly, over the Internet, where many youngsters, who have astutely come to recognize the awesome power and value of this newfangled technology to inflict profound harm upon their odious peers by publicly assassinating their character in widely disseminated messages to their equally odious friends, have made this droll form of entertainment a staple of their after-school social life.

T: You believe, then, that all gossip is malicious and harmful?

K: No, I don't. People obviously say kind and positive things about one another and even find ways to help each other during the course of their private confabs. But powwows between friends or co-workers would ordinarily not be worth the time and effort unless they were richly spiced with the condiment of malice and slanderous insinuation toward someone well out of earshot of the interlocutors. Yes, Dr. Taub, I'm afraid that most of us are untrustworthy quidnuncs to one degree or another.

T: Quidnunc? I don't know the word. What does it mean?

K: In Latin it means "What now?" A quidnunc is a newsmonger or busybody. It's one of my favorite words because it's so funny sounding. But to return to my point, I believe that feelings of hatred and animosity are as natural and ubiquitous as are the emotions of love and altruism in our culture and in the human personality. Yet most people, including my mother, find it hard, if not impossible, to accept this simple fact.

They must sugarcoat and whitewash over their own and other people's malevolent and evil intentions.

T: Like the time when your mother remarked that Uncle Bernie meant well when he was at same time scalping her?

K: Very good. I like emotionally strong language. Yes, my mother defended herself from her own rage by attributing to Uncle Bernie's scalpings benevolent intentions. But my mother was hardly unusual in this respect. If you listen carefully to the conversations of quite ordinary people in which they complain about the foul behavior of other individuals, you might notice that they will get up a good head of steam, blast away with hot expletives and denunciations, and then finish off their tirade with the absurd peroration that the son of a bitch meant well. Goodness knows what these people think would happen to them if they didn't tack on that silly pretension of forgiveness. Excommunication from their church? A godsent heart attack? An everlasting condemnation to hell? Acts of forgiveness can't be willed or conjured up like cupcakes from the oven. It requires time and great patience to heal and recover from the damage caused by extremely thoughtless people. Sometimes a single lifetime is simply not long enough to accomplish this Sisyphean feat. And if certain individuals simply cannot reach the requisite moral heights to forgive a perpetrator of an evil deed, then there is no moral wrong in their dying and being buried with hatred in their hearts for that person. I contend that they don't require moral redemption for their hatred. I certainly hope that Jews throughout the world would never find moral grounds to forgive Hitler for the monumental outrage of the Holocaust. Perhaps even some tinhorn tyrants, like my Uncle Bernie, should also not be forgiven their dirty tricks. But, as I said earlier, it's not for me to judge another person's willingness or unwillingness to forgive; everyone has the right to decide such things for themselves, without the impediment, by the way, of religious dogma and self-righteous moralists standing in their way.

T: Uncle Bernie still rankles you.

K: You bet. You know, to this day, whenever I hear someone say, "He meant well," I automatically assume two things: first, that the comment refers to a person who is behaving in an egregious manner and second, that the self-styled forgiver is lying (consciously or unconsciously, it doesn't matter). Over time I have come to the conclusion that "He meant well" is about the worst thing you can say about a person.

T: Why is that?

K: Because it is almost always said when it is impossible to think of any other redeeming qualities in the miscreant other than the one that has just been manufactured in fantasyland—that he meant well.

T: Does it matter if the person's misdeeds are committed consciously or unconsciously?

K: Not usually. If a person is physically or emotionally injured by another individual, it may, I will concede, matter to the victim whether the misdeed was committed intentionally or not, consciously or not. Perhaps the lack of intentionality will serve as an extenuation in the mind of the victim. But I must say that I have closely observed vast numbers of people who have been victimized by abusers and when they espouse their forgiveness for the perpetrator I find many of them entirely unconvincing. Why? Because some espouse their forgiveness too soon after their victimization; clearly, time and introspection have not been given sufficient opportunity to do their job. They prematurely and falsely espouse forgiveness because they clearly recognize that most of their fellow citizens, including the benighted majority who believe in hell and the devil, will applaud their saintly virtuousness, without giving thought to the possibility that forgiveness is being affirmed largely for the purpose of garnering social approval. I repeat, genuine forgiveness cannot be willed; it must emerge out of highly complicated thought processes that evolve very slowly and do not always complete their task. After all, some unspeakable acts of inhumanity and some unspeakably monstrous individuals simply do not merit anyone's forgiveness.

T: Is Uncle Bernie one such individual?

K: That's hard to answer. My mother probably found valid reasons to forgive his cruelty toward her. I never have. But perhaps I suffer from WDC, woeful deficiency of charitableness. But, Dr. Taub, do you know what else makes unalloyed forgiveness so ridiculously elusive, if not unattainable?

T: What?

K: Schadenfreude.

T: Why schadenfreude?

K: Think about it. Schadenfreude, the pleasure derived from the mishaps and misery of others, is a built-in component of the human personality, as essential to our survival, it seems, as our brain and vascular system. If we take just a cursory look at human life on this moribund planet of ours, we discover that ordinary people—not monsters, mind you—are everywhere reaping highly pleasurable gratification from the pain and suffering of other individuals.

T; Could you be more specific?

K: Easily. The first thing that comes to mind is contact sports, collegiate and professional football, for example. Players, in their more candid moments, will spill the beans about how much sadistic satisfaction they feel from slamming an opponent to the turf. If pain and an injury ensue, they rejoice, at least inwardly. The corporate world, which, as we know, can be a more ferocious arena than the football playing field, is another good example. When employers and supervisors, especially those that have administered departments with a heavy, whipping hand, get caught at some form of malfeasance such as stealing or fraud, their underlings will positively jubilate over the chagrin, anguish, demotion, or jail time the miscreants will have to suffer through.

More subtle and therefore more insidious are the ways in which even good friends will sometimes be suffused with schadenfreude over each other's misfortunes. Have you ever noticed how often people, upon learning of a friend's good fortune—a job promotion they received, a raffle they won in a contest, an acceptance letter they received from a publisher, the recent news of their child's academic or professional success—will feel downcast and then either change the subject or say something that disparages and devalues their friend's mood of celebration? Their obvious purpose is, patently, to transform their friend's good fortune into some form of misfortune by raining on their parade. This accounts for why so many people are inordinately reticent about disclosing with pride some of their significant personal achievements. Of course there are boasters who must showcase their accomplishments to everyone at all times, but let's put those odd characters aside for the moment. Most people, as far as I can tell, discover that when they are expressing pride over their especially successful and fulfilling experiences, their comments will soon be met by dismissive inattention or outright animosity in the form of repeated interruptions from others. That, Dr. Taub, is schadenfreude—the wish that others will have little over which to be exultant, but instead will live lives of quiet, unassuming, and bungling desperation.

T: You believe, then, that most individuals wish for their friends to be unhappy?

K: No, not always and not necessarily in the extreme. I can easily acknowledge that many people are quite generous in affirming the good qualities and achievements of others. But I am merely trying to explain why too often most people find it extremely difficult, if not impossible, to evoke from even good friends a solid, resonating affirmation that matches their own feelings of positive accomplishment. Again, I believe we're looking at envy and schadenfreude doing their mischievous handiwork.

Incidentally, since we're on the subject of hidden feelings of envy and schadenfreude, I probably should mention two of my favorite examples of how these emotions are disguised and turned on their heads in ordinary social conversations. Have you noticed, Dr. Taub, how often people will begin a sentence by saying to someone, "I don't mean to hurt your feelings but…"? I hope that by now most people would realize that whenever someone begins a sentence with those words that their foremost intention is to carry out the very thing they have disavowed: namely to hurt your feelings. And it happens every time. By the time they complete their sentence, their words contain enough castigating venom to kill an elephant or completely demoralize a person. The other opening phrase to look out for is "I don't wish him (or her) any harm, but..." This sentiment is ordinarily about as authentic as a seven-dollar bill. Count on it, Dr. Taub, anyone who uses such phraseology is camouflaging some pretty lethal thoughts. Their schadenfreude has been prettified to protect against the exposure of their dark side.

You know who was especially guilty of such emotional fraudulence, Dr. Taub? It was one of our nation's heroes, Will Rogers. One of his most oft-quoted statements was, "I never met a man I didn't like." I've heard this inane remark quoted hundreds of times throughout my life, usually in admiring and highly affectionate tones. Why? Because most people seem to believe that the capacity to like everyone one meets is not only humanly possible but, if attained, represents a blessed and exemplary state. Well, in my estimation it doesn't represent anything of the kind. It represents instead a form of ethical tone deafness and moral cowardice. What would Will Rogers have said after meeting, for example, Adolf Hitler, Joseph Stalin, Mussolini, Saddam Hussein or, going further back in time, Attila the Hun? Would he dare say, "I never met a genocidal dictator I didn't like?" There is simply no point in admiring everyone! A person who likes everyone has weak ethical standards or convictions. There are literally millions of very bad people on this planet: sociopaths, unregenerate sadists, and predators of all kinds. Are we supposed to like these people because Will Rogers would find it in his heart to do so? Well, maybe I'm being too harsh on poor old Will. Maybe he would have changed his mind and retracted his absurd remark, after all, had he actually met the psychopathic gods, Joe Stalin and Adolf Hitler. Then again, maybe, like my mother when discussing Uncle Bernie's sadism toward her, he might have found some way to extenuate their evil by claiming that at bottom they really meant well. But Will Rogers was no rube, so I still find it hard to explain or understand why he would espouse such nonsense. Let's face it, Dr. Taub, you can just as well take the ethical measure of most individuals by identifying the people they hate and avoid as much as by the people they love and esteem. And if I discover that someone genuinely and selectively hates certain individuals who repeatedly commit highly evil deeds, I will admire them for their courageous hatred.

T: I'm afraid we've run out of time today. I'd like to think further about the observations you've made regarding the dissembling ways in which people disguise and deny negative emotions like hatred. You have, I believe, identified your mother as a person who could not acknowledge her wrath or her resentments toward Uncle Bernie. It's no wonder you feel so impassioned about the need for emotional honesty in human relationships. What you heard from your mother about her angry feelings must have made you feel that she was living in a sham-world, and perhaps you felt that she was inviting you to join her in that sphere of self-deception.

K: I'm sorry that I've run overtime today, Dr. Taub. See you next time.

T: See you.

Professor Kittleman's Diary 6/19/06

Diary, what the hell is the matter with me? I used this session to give a discursive lecture on the human personality to an expert on the subject. Yes, I deeply believe in the things I said, but perhaps it's all a pile of intellectual bullshit. Why didn't Dr. Taub stop me by pointing out that I was rambling and most likely avoiding my deepest resentful feelings about being deceived by my mother? But how does one decide what's most important to talk about in a given psychotherapy session? Do all psychotherapeutic roads lead to Rome; that is, to some deeply buried mother lode of psychic gold?

I'm curious to know if Dr. Taub asked me my opinions about the universality of hatred, envy, and schandenfreude because he wanted to evoke more self-disclosure from me or if he was subtly disagreeing with my premises and arguments and didn't want to say so. I'd like to ask him, but I'm afraid I wouldn't get a straight answer; he'd probably volley back a question dealing with my motive for inquiring into his motives, which could, I imagine, lead to an ad infinitum entanglement.

The patient made an impassioned but largely well-reasoned analysis of the dark side of humankind. The intensity and preoccupation he feels about emotionally fraudulent behavior—the tendency of the average person to dissimulate, especially when it comes to the matter of acknowledging feelings of envy, hatred, and schadenfreude—have deep roots in his relationship with his mother, who was an artful dodger of such emotions. So far, the patient has not discussed his wife or father in any depth or detail, so for the time being I am getting an asymmetrical view of the psychodynamics of the Kittleman family.

For the most part, the patient's grasp of the disguising defense mechanisms that are manifested in everyday life were, in my estimation, sound and perspicacious. I think, however, I need to guard myself against a countertransference tendency to become more interested in the subject under discussion than in the patient and his underlying psychic conflicts. I must stand ready, if necessary, to interpret his intellectual digressions as a defense against dealing with emotional pain.

K: Dr. Taub, I want to mention that I had a few misgivings about our last session.

T: What were your misgivings, specifically?

K: Well, I'm having difficulty figuring out whether I'm using my time here productively enough. For example, the topic I discussed in our last session was of considerable importance to me, but that doesn't make it truly relevant to my emotional conflicts, does it?

T: That's true, but quite often we can't know or predict the value of any given session until we have reached a later phase in the therapy.

K: So, I may be worrying unnecessarily. Is that what you're saying?

T: Perhaps your worries are exaggerated, but even so, they too should be carefully discussed and analyzed.

K: I suppose I feel on some level that I must meet your expectations, whatever they may be. I know I've left several sessions feeling that I have disappointed you.

T: In what respect?

K: I want to be a "good" patient. No, that's wrong. I want to be your "best" patient. I know it's an infantile wish, but I want you to be proud of me. I want to make such exemplary progress in the therapy that one day you will be inspired to write an article for a professional journal about our work together. I know this peculiar disclosure comes from out of the blue, so to speak, but I'm trying to be as candid and open as I can about my feelings toward you and the therapy and I thought this would be a good place to start. Now I'm feeling a bit jittery.

T: How so?

K: Something from the past, I'm not sure what it is, makes me feel that I can't fully trust your judgment to protect me from harm now that I've placed myself in your care.

T: Take a moment to think it over. Does anything come to mind about someone betraying your trust in such a way as to cause you significant harm?

K: Now that I think of it, the catchwords "betrayal" and "harm" conjure up an experience I had when I was 12 and in grade school. Perhaps it's worth sharing with you. I don't know. What do you think?

T: I think you're asking me for permission to tell me something you wish to tell me and wonder why you need a go-ahead from me in order to relate your experience. Perhaps you're concerned that I might not be sufficiently interested in this experience or even sufficiently interested in you to want to hear about it. You said you wanted to be my best patient. Perhaps this is your way of testing my desire to make you my best, my most self-disclosing, patient.

K: You may be right, but your interpretation may be a bit too sophisticated and premature for my sluggish brain to grasp at this time. But I'll infer from what you've just said that it might be advantageous for me to tell you the betrayal/harm experience. Okay?

T: Are you still asking my permission?

K: Not any more. Here goes. I grew up in the Central Ward of Newark, New Jersey. By 1950, when I was 12, the streets below Hunterdon Street, the street of our residence, were largely inhabited by black families. In the late '40s and early '50s the homogeneously black community ended one block short of Hunterdon Street, which caused some of the families on our block to view our row of houses as the hindmost white bastion to protect the rest of the city from the swelling black hordes. In the post-war years black migration from the South accelerated and, consequently, there was among Jewish families, such as ours, increased anxiety and talk about the "*schvartzes*" (the rather derogatory Yiddish word for blacks).

Much to their credit, my parents were not virulently prejudiced against blacks and I, therefore, received no advice or strictures from them as to how I was to conduct myself with "colored" kids.

I attended Waverly Avenue Grammar School, which, according to an inscription on a plaque hanging near its front entrance, was built in 1886. Contiguous with the main building was a three-storey stairwell enclosed in brick, which, when viewed from the outside, looked like a well-fortified prairie silo.

This antiquated and misshapen school was staffed predominantly by hard-working, up-in-years schoolmarms, a few of whom, I suspected, had been in attendance at the groundbreaking ceremonies in 1886. The vice-principal of Waverly was Mr. Goldstein, a soft-spoken and benign administrator who had taken a liking to me, perhaps because I was Jewish and the number of Jewish kids attending that school was dwindling exponentially each year. Actually, Mr. Goldstein was the de facto principal much of the year since Mrs. Barth, the officious, granite-jawed principal, also served as the top administrator of Tenth Street School where, thank goodness, she spent most of her time.

The incongruous team of Goldstein-Barth came to play a major part in my maldevelopment as a child. As result of being reasonably popular with my peers and a close friend of the former chief of our school patrol force, I was elected in my last year at Waverly to the position of chief of the patrol service. My job was to supervise the other patrol officers, kids like myself, on their respective beats at the busy intersections in the neighborhood of the school. Soon after my election as chief I was called into Mrs. Barth's office, where I was notified by her and the avuncular Mr. Goldstein that, by dint of my new and prestigious position as chief of the school patrol force, I was being chosen to carry out an unusual assignment.

It seemed that a boy named Timothy Jones, a notoriously tough and cantankerous black youth, had been a chronic truant for the past term. The school officials believed they were being manipulated and hoodwinked by Timothy's transparently forged letters into excusing him from school for bogus illnesses and doctors' appointments. In order to firmly establish his delinquency, Mrs. Barth and Mr. Goldstein deemed it necessary for someone to witness and report Timothy playing on the streets during school hours. They jointly decided that I, as an eminently reliable patrol captain, should assume this honorific responsibility. I was naturally pleased and flattered to be chosen for this assignment and within a few minutes I was being sent off on my heroic mission by two smiling well-wishers who, almost as an aside, cautioned me to try my best not to be observed by Timothy and his friends while I sleuthed about the streets looking for him.

Within one hour I was back at Waverly reporting to Goldstein/Barth that I had indeed seen Timothy and his friends frolicking in the street near his home and, to the best of my knowledge, they had not taken note of me. I then returned to class inflated by the warm congratulatory remarks and hardy backslaps I received from the two jubilant co-conspirators.

On my way home from school that afternoon, while turning the corner of Bergen Street and 18th Avenue, I descried in the distance a large band of black kids tromping militarily up the hill, each holding a loaded burlap sack in his hand. For a moment the import of this spectacle was not apparent to me. I soon realized that in the vanguard of this fearsome phalanx marched Timothy Jones, who was animatedly hooting and gesturing in my direction. Above the street noise I could hear him shout my name.

Realizing the horrible truth that I was the intended quarry of this gang of marauders bestirred me to make a dash for my house, which was a good 50 yards away. This was a perilous course since I had no choice but to run in the direction of Jones and company in order to reach Hunterdon Street and, therefore, take the chance that they might intercept me before I reached my house.

I managed to make my front door perhaps 15 seconds before my pursuers. In my terror I couldn't readily find my key so I began to beat furiously on the door and the windows while shouting for help. The front door suddenly opened and my mother emerged. By this time the mob had made its way halfway up the 12 steps of our porch and when I turned around I viewed clearly for the first time the awful threat I had just narrowly escaped. There on the steps were three of Jones's confederates followed by at least seven others who were still in the street. Each of them was carrying a large burlap sack in his hand, laden with heavy, bulging rocks. One of the more brazen of the bunch was a walleyed youngster who advanced menacingly up the steps even after my mother, who was carrying a broomstick and looking pretty menacing herself, had made it clear that she was going to defend her beloved Sheldon to the death, if necessary. The walleyed sack-wielder was particularly petrifying due to his crazily divergent eyes that gave his overall countenance a reptilian, atavistic look. Finally, Timothy Jones, evidently realizing the potential gravity of the situation, ordered his troops to withdraw.

Within a few minutes the would-be assailants had retreated out of sight. That evening my parents held a high-strung and lengthy discussion about poor Sheldon's harrowing escape from being stoned to smithereens. My parents, who naturally knew nothing of my heroic expedition for Goldstein/Barth, theorized that I was a chance victim of hooligans who were randomly looking for a vulnerable white scapegoat. I knew better. I understood that Timothy had somehow found out that I had conspired against him and was seeking justifiable and, in his view, proportionate revenge. I also realized that I had been badly duped by Goldstein/Barth and by my own naiveté into doing something detrimental to another Waverly student that, had it been absolutely necessary, would better have been assigned to a professional truant officer. Because I felt stupid and ashamed of my prideful gullibility, I kept the matter of my conspiracy with Mr. Goldstein and Mrs. Barth a secret from my parents.

When I returned to school the next day, there were many rumors being bruited about, the gist of which was that sooner or later Timothy Jones would make me pay heavily for my treachery. Timothy himself did not return to Waverly, however, and, according to one believable report, he was sent to a nearby reformatory. For many days I walked the streets with great stealth and slept fitfully until it became fairly evident that Timothy was either too confined or too distracted to carry out his vendetta.

I had heard nothing more of Timothy Jones over the next decade or so, although he and his sack-carrying cohorts would involuntarily return to my thoughts many times in the ensuing years, and always with disruptive effect. In 1964, roughly 13 years later, Timothy and I were reunited under strange, almost surrealistic circumstances. I had been working as a volunteer in a state mental hospital where one day, as I approached the administration building, a police car drove up with a large, husky black man sitting in the rear behind a metal partition. Our eyes met glancingly and I recognized him immediately. I don't know whether Timothy recognized me, since he returned only an impassive stare. As I later discovered, he was to be confined in the maximum-security unit, a facility set aside for the so-called criminally insane. I also learned from a social worker in that unit that he had first been incarcerated in a state prison where he had set fire to his cell and, following a psychiatric evaluation, was transferred to the maximum security unit where he was deemed to be a dangerously disturbed person. I passed him once in a ward of the maximum-security unit and had a fleeting opportunity to speak with him, if I chose. Fear, shame, and remorse overcame me and I passed on without a sign or word of greeting. I still sometimes find myself wishing to know more about the events of Timothy's past, including the one in which I was fortuitously implicated, so I could better understand how this man came to live such a gnarled and miserable life.

T: So you went through a harrowing, almost fatal experience because two incompetent and irresponsible school administrators decided to put you in the path of danger in order to authenticate another student's truancy record.

K: That's about right, Dr. Taub, although I wouldn't label Mr. Goldstein an incompetent. Although I was no judge at the time, I remember that almost everyone, including myself, liked the man very much. He ran the school with a progressive Deweyan touch. He was, I believe, quite competent. But in this one instance he failed to use common sense to such an egregious degree that he nearly had me stoned to death. That is what I sometimes find quite appalling; how good, intelligent, and quite competent people can now and then do unconscionable things to others without being at all aware of the monumental harm they are inflicting upon them. My mother would, of course, say that Mr. Goldstein meant well when he tried to track down Timothy Jones with my help and there-fore should be forgiven.

I would agree that the vice-principal's intentions were principled—in deference to my mother of course—but he will never receive my forgive-ness for the many sleepless nights I suffered as a kid and for the horrific images I still see in my mind's eye when I recall how I might have been maimed for life or even killed—all because two educational officials used me as a stalking-horse to catch their quarry truanting. No one, least of all a professional educator, should ever do that to a kid.

T: Absolutely. It's bad enough when bad people do bad things to kids. It can be much worse when someone you like, trust, and respect—Mr. Goldstein, in this case—betrays you and endangers your life in the way he and Mrs. Barth did. I'm sorry, but our time is up. We'll have to stop.

K: I feel positively about the fact that I was able to share some of my conflicted feelings about you early in the session. I believe it would be beneficial if I could continue to do that in our future sessions. See you next time.

Professor Kittleman's Diary 6/25/06

Diary, what the hell is the matter with me? Session after session I bitch to you about the fact that I can't be forthright in my sessions with Dr. Taub. Then I walk in and impulsively blurt out a few puerile inanities about how I want to be his most spectacular clinical success story. I made a fool out of myself in there and then I leapt in to sugarcoat my blunder by telling him I would find it beneficial if I could make a few more idiotic gaffes during our sessions. Okay, diary, maybe I'm being too hard on myself. Maybe, just maybe, I displayed a modicum of courage by telling him the truth; by letting him know that I suffer from some loopy form of infantilism that makes me crave grandeur and celebrity, even if it must be vicariously experienced through the stellar achievements of my therapist. But telling Dr. Taub that I feared disappointing him and had wished for him to knight me as his finest success story is not the same thing as telling him that I cyclically wish to kill him during and between our sessions.

For several evenings after relating the Timothy Jones tale I slept restlessly, although my dreams did not concoct horrific images of violent, stone-bearing marauders, as they did when I was a youngster. Maybe I'm on my way, at last, to casting off some of the residual vulnerability connected with that nasty episode. At least I hope so, diary. By the way, I found, after venting my spleen at Mr. Goldstein in the last session, that my earlier feelings of fondness for him returned along with some sludgy seepage of forgiveness. Is this suggestion of forgiveness for him some of my mother's neurotic handiwork or is it the real thing, and are the two things necessarily mutually exclusive? In other words, can my mother still have a profound effect upon the way I think and feel without her ongoing influence transforming me into a specious, inauthentic person?

The patient made an unheralded stab at verbalizing his concerns about the nature of our relationship with specific reference to his wishes that I embrace him as so unique and special a person that he would become the subject of one of my journal articles trumpeting a successful therapy. These narcissistic wishes have their roots, I suspect, in repeated and significant parental failures to celebrate the patient's uniqueness as a child.

Since the patient's psychogenetic history is as yet rather sparse, he and I will need to fill in the gaps in his past before I can identify and interpret the specific ways in which parental invalidation took place. The patient related in this session a harrowing, life-threatening episode (which took place when he was 12) involving a mob of children who were evidently bent on killing him—and would have succeeded had it not been for his mother's rather brazen, last-minute intervention. This traumatic experience was brought about because of the gross ineptitude of two grade school administrators who sent the patient out on a fact-finding, bell-the-cat mission to snag a truanting fellow student, a responsibility that should have been rightly assigned to a professional truant officer. The patient's sense of betrayal was heightened afterward by the fact that one of these administrators was someone he had liked and deeply trusted. I detected in the patient's defense of the administrator's character that he still harbors a fondness for the man.

Ninth Session 6/29/06

K: I don't quite know where to begin today. I suppose I should tell you that I came away from our last session feeling downcast. I thought I had made a fool of myself when I told you that I wanted to be celebrated by you as your most spectacularly successful case. To be sure, that impulsive disclosure of my grandiosity represented a momentary lapse into complete and, who knows, even revitalizing candor, but I'm not used to betraying my juvenility to other people. Even though I know that you, as a casehardened therapist, have heard that kind of claptrap and worse from hundreds of your patients and will not unduly judge or ridicule me, I still fear that I had revealed a facet of my personality that I might prefer to keep hidden in a closet somewhere. You know, Dr. Taub, I have come to believe that one of the deepest fears suffered by us narcissists is our fear that our narcissism—with its hallmarks of grandiosity, hypersensitivity to personal slights, a woeful inability to regulate self-esteem, a solipsistic self-centeredness, a marked lack of empathy and a tendency to demean and devalue others that pisses off and alienates practically everybody—will be discovered and identified for what it is, the wish to be viewed and treated like a fucking emperor. But this emperor, as we know, is shorn of clothing. Yet he wants others to wink at his nakedness, not see that he wants the world to revolve around and harmonize with his every exquisite need and wish. It is his tragedy that he must be ever vigilant in order to disguise his utter selfishness from others lest he will lose their veneration and esteem. It's such a tragic thing, isn't it, Dr. Taub, for a narcissist to spend an entire life feigning moral probity and authenticity while the imprisoned, enfeebled self that forms the core of his character insatiably searches for celebrity and adoration from others simply in order to survive?

T: Are you suggesting that you are such a tragic narcissist yourself?

K: I don't think so, at least not in the extreme form I have described. But I am accoutered, so to speak, with enough narcissistic traits to clinically qualify as one and to get myself in sufficient trouble with other people. Why else would I have exposed myself—the pinnacle of narcissism, I think you would agree—to a multitude of college professors and administrators on that inglorious day that ended my career as a public speaker?

T: These traits of narcissism, what or who does that make you think of?

K: That's easy, Dr. Taub; my father, the inveterate narcissist. You know, a few years before he died—he must have been about 89 at the time—he was visiting us. By that time I had mentally stockpiled quite a number of grievances over his past ill treatment of me. I had no intention of enumerating or rehashing some of these unpleasant experiences, but I did want to gain from him some perspective and perhaps some acknowledgement of how his repeated acts of selfishness had hurt me. So, finding him in a relaxed mood, I popped a relevant question, an icebreaker, you might say. I said, "Dad, take a moment to think about this. Do you ever remember having made a mistake of any kind in raising me?" He gave me a befuddled look, paused for just a few moments, and then replied, "No, I can't think of anything." "Nothing?" I rejoined. He just sat there and silently shook his head. He then asked me the time, as if by establishing the hour as having primary importance he could shoo away my pain and my question. He did this in the petulant and unthinking way one might flick away a pesky fly. Trying as hard as I could to harness my anger, I followed up with a more pointed question, one I asked in a voice dripping, I could tell, with sarcasm. "Dad, are you really telling me that you were a perfect father?" Again, he looked at me with an expression of perplexity. But he wasted no time in answering this question. "Yes, Sheldon, as far as I can tell, I was a perfect father. Do you disagree by any chance?" By this time my blood was aboil and I wanted to strangle him to death. The unmitigated chutzpah of this man was actually endangering his life. Well, maybe I'm exaggerating, but I do remember how I wanted to seize and sever the carotid artery that was by now bulging in his wizened neck. I then found some way, I don't know how, to collect my thoughts and feelings enough to use words rather than my hands to deal with his insulting overconfidence. I began to…

T: Excuse me. You mentioned that your father was 89 at the time. Do you think he would have answered your questions with that kind of dismissive pomposity had he been a much younger man with sturdier faculties?

K: I see what you're driving at. Perhaps his failure to acknowledge his limitations as a parent was a function of some form of age-related organicity, which might be adduced as an extenuation. If so, my badgering him with hostile exhortations to fess up about his parental screw-ups was unfair and cruel. Perhaps I was being unfair. I suppose I thought, given my father's advanced years, that I had only one last chance before he died to garner from him some expression of regret over how he had often neglected and mistreated me. Had he come through, I probably would have accepted that acknowledgment as a token of his love for me. When he stubbornly withheld his acknowledgment of wrongdoing—and his love—the pain I felt drove me to launch into a tirade about his long history of parental blunders. I was about to tell you about that tirade when you asked me if I thought his rigidly held view of his perfection as a father was a function of organic enfeeblement or, instead, a lifelong character trait. I'd prefer to think that some of his rigid stubbornness at 89 was attributable to his age, but I knew the man well from harsh first-hand experience and I can confidently attest to the fact that he always believed himself to be perfectly flawless and unassailable in all respects. What he had pompously asserted about himself at 89 he had fervently believed when he was 39, 49, 59, 69, and 79. The assertion that he was loftily above all criticism and blame was one of his most disgusting and infuriating characteristics, I can assure you.

T: You were about to tell me what you had said to him in a tirade.

K: I think, Dr. Taub, that before I do that it might be best if I first provided you with some background about my father's life, if that's okay. It will, I'm sure, help to explain his character and behavior as a parent and at the same time shed some useful light on the checkered course of my own life.

T: Of course.

K: My father was born in 1899 in the Southeastern region of Poland then known as Galicia. At the time it was a part of the Austro-Hungarian Empire. My dad's parents owned an inn and stable in a hamlet known as Rosperz de Lugy, if I am recalling the pronunciation of the name correctly. The stable rented out horses and the inn served meals and boarded transient guests, some of whom were soldiers stationed in the area. According to my father, it was a flourishing business and for a long while family life was on an even keel. Around 1908 my grandfather discerned that large numbers of troops were amassing in the vicinity of his town and he took that, correctly it seems, to be an early harbinger of war. Thus, he began contriving plans to resettle his family of seven young children and a wife in America.

His plan to leave Poland received an unexpected fillip when my grandfather secreted a suspected felon in one of his horse-drawn wagons to a sanctuary out of the reach of the governmental authorities who wanted to arrest and imprison him. Apparently my grandfather's complicity in the man's escape was leaked to a police office and it was vaguely rumored that he, too, might be arrested and jailed. The threat of prosecution forced my grandfather to make hurried plans to decamp. Because their inn was still raking in a substantial income, he was reluctant to close it down and leave with the entire family. Reasoning that the three youngest children would be better off with their mother, he swept up the four eldest and immediately emigrated to the U.S. with them, with the proviso that my grandmother and the three youngest would follow them within a year. My father remained behind and assumed the role of surrogate dad to his two younger sisters.

True to his word, my grandfather sent for his wife and kids within 10 months. My father, grandmother, and aunts were taken by wagon to a nearby railway depot where they boarded a train to Hamburg, Germany, the port of embarkation. While in Hamburg the ship's passengers were billeted at a local hostelry. With great pride my father has told me many times how his mother entrusted him to sleep with and guard the sizeable nest egg she was bringing with her to America. My father stealthily placed his cache beneath his pillow before going to sleep. In the middle of the night there was an alarum—screams about a fire—that awakened everyone. In a great chaotic scramble people jumped out of bed, grabbed their clothes and evacuated the premises. When they arrived outside, they discovered to their dismay that the alarum was a ruse, a pretext for separating the hapless evacuees from their possessions. In a panic they raced back to their beds only to discover the ghastly truth: their most prized possessions had been stolen. My father, however, had had the foresight and *sachel* to take the cache his mother had entrusted to him from underneath the pillow before leaving the building. This story was always told with an, "I knew even as a nine-year-old kid better than to leave my mother's money in that godforsaken building" smirk on his face. I suppose, now that I think of it, he was entitled to that smirk for rescuing his mother's hard-earned savings.

Anyway, they landed in New York at Ellis Island where they were processed and later authorized to enter the country. A train took them to Newark, where my grandfather had already set up a new business, a stable that rented out horses, just like in the old country sans the inn. My father vividly remembered, even at 89, how the reunion took place. He, his mother and two sisters found the street of my grandfather's residence without much difficulty. From a distance they espied him sitting on the porch. As they approached, my father observed that my grandfather was eating strawberries. This is all he ever said about this reunion; not a word about expressions or gestures of affection, only that his father was eating strawberries.

I never knew my grandfather and, based on what I have learned about him over the years, I can't say that constituted a serious loss in my life. He died about five years before I was born. I have seen only one photograph of him. The camera captures a man with an impassive, unsmiling, almost menacing, expression. He wore a long white beard that extended well below the scapula, reminding me of the Smith brothers as they appeared on their cough drop boxes many years ago.

One of grandpa's most distinguishing characteristics was his violence. My father worked in the stable tending to the horses. Each day he rode to school on a horse, which caused him great shame as he entered his classes carrying horse-fetor on his clothing. Worst of all, however, was my grandfather's active and pugnacious opposition to my father's pursuit of schooling. My father liked school, where he learned to read and speak English rather quickly and wanted to remain as long as possible. One day he was late for work at the stable. When his father questioned him about his tardiness, he explained that a teacher had delayed him with an assignment. His father went into a rage, told him that an education in the schools was middling as compared to the good practical education he would receive working in the family business. With that, he smacked my father across the face. My father suffered a lifelong visual impairment from that smack. My dad left school at the age of 11 to work in the stables and help support the family.

But Grandpa Kittleman's violence did not stop with hitting the children. He was an inveterate wife-beater as well. By the time my father had reached adolescence and had left home, he was receiving reports from his younger siblings that grandpa's abusiveness had reached even greater and more dangerous proportions. Grandma had twice moved out of the house to escape further endangerment and then, after being cajoled by grandpa with promises of atonement, she went back to him, only, of course, to go through another, and even more violent, round of debasing misusage. Finally, my father, by this time almost fully grown and definitely a physical match for his smallish father, went to the house with a message, actually, a lethal ultimatum. He told grandpa that if he ever laid his hands on his mother again he would kill him. As far as my father knew, that ended the wife-beating in a flash.

After leaving home and the stables, Dad worked as a counterman in the Jewish delicatessens of Prince Street and its environs, the erstwhile Jewish neighborhood of Newark. He liked the work but soon discovered that more gainful employment could be found in the dry cleaning business. For the most part he worked for men like himself; immigrants with limited formal education but endowed with steadfast ambitions to better themselves socially and economically, leave behind the squalor of the city ghetto, afford a luxurious home either in the Weequahic section or in the suburbs, and send their kids to the best colleges. What distinguished my father from these men, however, had little to do with ambition, industriousness, business acumen, or intelligence. In my view, based on what I have heard and seen first-hand, my father could not rise to the level of owner-entrepreneur of a lucrative dry cleaning establishment mainly because he lacked foresight, not ambition. He simply could not foresee that the course he had chosen would take him down the marginal, precarious path of penury. Well, penury is probably too strong a word. He and my mother led a hardscrabble life, to be sure, but there was always food on the table and the bills were always paid, albeit tardily now and then. But their on-the-edge-of-penury situation led to many battles royal between them and this nightly exchange of cutting sarcasms and denigrations—always fought over the theme of being on the brink of financial disaster—left them emotionally exhausted and me in a state of fearing the possible dissolution of their marriage followed by my being cast off as a costly burden and adopted by anonymous chicken farmers in South Jersey.

In any event, my father did not become an owner-entrepreneur of a dry cleaning establishment until he was in his late 50s. As you may remember from the letter I sent you, he took on two successive partners who were bird-brained liabilities, two outrageous schmucks he quickly had to jettison in order to save the business. He soloed that business through some bad financial storms, with occasional and grudging help from my mother and me, until he retired at the age of 65.

Professor Kittleman's Therapy

T: You said that he was industrious, ambitious, and intelligent. Yet he lacked, in your view, vision and foresight. What makes you think so?

K: My father, I can proudly say, was an adept at every aspect of the cleaning business. He could press clothes with the best of them. He also knew precisely how to use cleaning products—those admixed chemicals that he placed in a noisy tumbler with the dirty clothes and emitted a nauseatingly sweet smell that was simply overpowering on hot summer days. He also knew something about dyeing clothes and when so inclined he could display considerable talents as a tailor as well. He must have watched and learned carefully from his bosses and co-workers throughout his apprenticeship in that industry. But it didn't get him very far.

T: But why do you say it was a lack of foresight that was his undoing?

K: Dr. Taub, I don't know whether you've ever read Jack London's story "To Build a Fire," but it brilliantly depicts the essence of my father's dilemma. A man enters the frozen wilderness of the Yukon with a dog. He carries matches to build a fire but is thoughtlessly underdressed for the bitter storm that overtakes him. After accidentally getting his feet wet and frozen, he sets out to thaw them by building a fire. Oblivious to the senselessness of his actions, he builds the fire under a snow-laden tree. The snow in the tree melts and collapses upon the fire, extinguishing it. From that point on the man's plight becomes hopeless and he eventually must resign himself to the inevitability of dying. "To Build a Fire" is London's brilliantly depicted tale of a person who is afflicted with a fatal flaw: an abysmal dearth of foresight and imagination. My father was afflicted with this selfsame flaw. He repeatedly kindled the fires of his dearest hopes and ambitions in the wrong places, ignoring telltale signs of impediment and danger. As, for example, when he yoked himself to those two slugabed partners, the Communist who disavowed profit and the gambler who pursued profits galore through games of chance. As, for another example, when he refused to allow my mother to go out and find a job.

T: What was that about?

K: Before they were married my mother was a typist-secretary in an office at Newark City Hall. She typed on one of those old, clunky manuals at the brisk clip of 90 words a minute. She was good at her work and she liked it. But my father, narcissist and misogynist nonpareil, thought it was a blow to his exalted persona to have his wife working out of the home and, worse, earning an income that might match or even surpass his own. He did, however, "allow" her to undertake a short stint of employment at the downtown post office each holiday season, sorting the huge avalanche of mail that came into that building toward the end of the year and earning enough to provide my parents with a financial cushion going into the next year. Many years later my father boasted to me about his role in squelching my mother's employment prospects. It seems that my mother liked the work at the post office so much that she decided to apply for a full-time job there. When she mentioned this to my father, he became incensed and declared her too unqualified for such a position. Undaunted, my mother insisted that she would submit an application. It happened that the application arrived in the mail on a day when my father had briefly stopped by the house on his way back to the shop. He recognized the letter containing the application sent by the post office. He opened it, gave the application a quick once-over, and then tore it and the envelope into tiny, unrecognizable scraps. My mother, after having her job application form clandestinely interdicted by my father, evidently thought the post office had changed its mind about her qualifications. She never again brought up the subject and settled for her holiday work, sorting mail.

T: And you say that he boasted about deceiving and undermining your mother in this way?

K: Yes, he told me this story with a diabolical grin on his face, all the while hugging himself with pride for his ingenuity in fucking up my mother's hopes to better herself.

T: Those are the traits that you refer to as narcissistic. But what about the role his lack of education and vocational opportunity, especially during the Depression years, played in thwarting his hopes and ambitions?

K: I don't wish to minimize or trivialize those important obstacles in his life. That would much too uncharitable. I realize that—and here I am talking about the time when my father was a young man—many of his compatriots were, like himself, poorly educated and economically disadvantaged. And some of these men became quite successful, at least in the material sense, not necessarily because they possessed vision and imagination, but by dint of happenstance and nepotism. But I still contend that my father and the nameless man in London's story bethought themselves immune from danger and vulnerability and it was that grandiose, narcissistic trait, more than anything else, which stood in the way of my father's capacity to realistically confront adversity.

T: How, exactly, would you define your father's adversity?

K: As I've said, our family did not suffer from actual poverty or severe deprivation. No, it wasn't poverty that plagued our family and led to the battles royal between my parents. It was, instead, the specter of poverty that infused my parents with fear, envy, and vituperative resentment. I understood this very well and therefore did not resent our lack of material comforts per se. I was well clothed and fed and was even given a moderate allowance each week that I would spend on candy, Italian hot dogs, or matinees at the Ritz Theater on Springfield Avenue. My own resentment, Dr. Taub, has always and mainly been over those damn nightly parental brawls that scared and repulsed me.

L: You mentioned something about envy a moment ago.

K: Yes. Envy played a very important role in instigating my mother's humiliating attacks upon my father. You see, most of my maternal grandmother's siblings somehow became quite wealthy in the banking and bakery business. This meant that my mother's cousins, the offspring of my grandmother's affluent siblings, were living on easy street most of their life. My mother kept a watchful eye on the ascending wealth and status of her cousins and never spoke of them without spicing her remarks with a few chosen aspersions about their snobbish, uppity ways. My father, with his meager income as a dry cleaner, provided my mother with a drab lifestyle that humiliated her whenever she pondered the opulence of her cousins—which, if memory serves me correctly, was about every five waking minutes. So she took her humiliation out on my father by disparaging him something awful. I suppose she didn't subscribe to the belief expressed by the poor tailor in *Fiddler on the Roof*, who told Tevye, his future father-in-law, that even a lowly tailor is entitled to a life of respect and dignity.

T: We're going to need to stop soon but I'd like to share a thought or two about the memories you shared during this session. My impression of the painful struggles you experienced over your parents' economic marginality and their constant bickering is that they aroused in you the horror of physical and emotional abandonment, whether it was in the form of an adoption by South Jersey chicken farmers or perhaps something far worse. A young child often has exaggerated fears of being abandoned by its parents, but this fear can be especially acute when a child has two parents who are often hateful and disparaging toward each other because their relationship is easily and often justifiably viewed by the child as tenuous. It is no wonder you have felt over the years such strong resentment for their stunted ability to cope with adversity, as you had earlier stated in this session.

K: Thank you. I'd like to share a few more recollections of my father in our next session. They will perhaps shed further light on how his personality and behavior shaped my life, particularly with respect to my fear of abandonment. See you next time.

Professor Kittleman's Diary 6/30/06

Diary, I really stuck it to my father in this session. Was I excessive and unfair in my characterization of him as a misogynist and narcissist? Hell, the guy could have been a lot worse. He never took to drink, he didn't beat his son or his wife like his old man had, he worked hard since his early boyhood, his educational and vocational opportunities were limited by straitened circumstances and, it should be noted, in his lighter moments he could be kind and hilariously funny. I recall when, shortly before he died, he visited Ethel and me. On a lark we took Dad to an amusement park where there was an expansive wooden maze that visitors entered and meandered through until their navigational ingenuity enabled them to gain egress at some distant point from the entrance. The walk through the maze was stiflingly monotonous and the weather, cold and damp, didn't help. After about a half hour we decided to call it quits and left by the emergency exit. Later, sitting in a coffee shop, I asked Dad how he had liked our little diversion in the maze. With a mischievous twinkle in his eye he said that he liked it so much that he intended, after his death, to return to the goddamned place to haunt it as a ghost. He then followed that witticism with another: "You know," he quipped, "it cost us eight dollars apiece to get lost in that maze. If I wanted, I could walk out of my apartment in Clark, New Jersey, and get lost in no time and it wouldn't cost me a cent." This, in my view, is brilliant extemporaneous humor. Of course, diary, his humor could be cutting and hurtful at times, as when we were standing outside the monkey cage at the San Francisco Zoo. A woman caretaker of the monkeys was feeding and cradling them in her arms. My father noticed that the woman was decidedly physically unattractive and he seized the opportunity to say, audibly enough for her and several bystanders to hear (by that time he was quite hard of hearing and therefore underestimated the ability of others to hear him), "No wonder she loves monkeys, with her looks she could never make it with a man." I was horrified with embarrassment and acted, unconvincingly I'm sure, as if I didn't know the crazed man.

I suppose I'm entirely entitled to my negative thoughts and emotions about my father, disproportionate or overblown as they may be; especially in therapy where there is no such thing as a "bad" thought or feeling. Isn't the moral neutrality of the therapist and the therapeutic milieu one of therapy's primary curative agents? Well, diary, let's get real. No therapist is truly morally neutral. It is true, of course, that if therapists are doing their job well, they will suspend moral judgment of their patients for about as long as the sessions last. But afterward, who knows what moralistic notions they have toward their struggling charges that they never dare to verbalize to them? Which reminds me: I thought Dr. Taub, when he asked me if my father's disappointing (to me) achievements were due to the paucity of educational and vocational opportunities of the time, spoke in a tone of asperity that carried the weight of moral judgment. In other words, I felt that he thought my moral judgments of my father were excessive and that I should have tossed a long, merciful, rescuing rope of extenuation to Dad. At this point, I'm simply not ready for that and I felt annoyed with Dr. Taub for goading me in that way. After all, I'm not matriculating in the course "The Social Psychology of the Jewish Immigrant during the Great Depression" with Dr. Taub, and I don't need factual reminders from him about the hardships my father and other poor immigrants faced in this country. Dad's personality was profoundly shaped by those hardships but they don't, in my view, completely acquit him of his many acts of cruel thoughtlessness toward me.

I should mention that Dr. Taub's observation of my abandonment fears during my parents' fights rang true and will, I expect, help me better understand my never-ending rage over their nightly squabbles. Notwithstanding the annoyance I felt over his reminders about my father's societally based adversities, I very much appreciated the empathy he evinced in identifying a core fear of mine. Now if I could only stop wanting to kill the man.

In this session the patient first provided a rather clear description of his father's childhood experiences as an immigrant. Apparently, the patient's paternal grandfather was a tyrannical and physically abusive man who did untold physical and emotional harm to his wife and children, including, of course, the patient's father. During his childhood the patient's father was a barely adequate breadwinner and the internecine verbal battles between husband and wife left the patient feeling that their marriage would fail and lead to his being deserted by them. This, fortunately, did not happen but the patient has harbored a smoldering resentment ever since toward his parents, especially his father, over the pain and fear their fights engendered in him. The patient was receptive to my interpretation regarding his fears of abandonment, but I suspect silently demurred when I implied that his father's personal limitations were the common casualties of a whole generation of poor, neglected immigrants. This intervention was probably construed by the patient as an attempt on my part to not just extenuate but excuse and justify his father's narcissistic acts of thoughtlessness. This ill-advised intervention bespeaks the importance of staying within the realm of the patient's subjective emotional world as much as possible rather than prematurely insinuating the objective facts and verities of life that exist in the "real" world into the therapy. I will look for and anticipate signs of the patient's adverse reactions to what he will probably consider to be my lapse of empathy.

K: I mentioned at the end of our last session, Dr. Taub, my wish to continue discussing my father. So, without further ado, I'll just jump in. My father, soon after he married my mother, was induced by his father-in-law to join an organization of men all of whom emigrated from the same general area of Europe—Galicia. The raison d'etre of this organization was its charitable service to the poor, sick, and dying, and their bereft families. Meetings were held on a monthly basis and my father and grandfather were regular attendees. Eventually, my father was appointed or volunteered to be chairman of the so-called burial committee. This assignment entailed assisting the family of the deceased with burial arrangements, including, quite often, a subvention covering the costs of the funeral service, cemetery plot, and casket. The organization owned and maintained its own cemetery, thus it managed to keep overall funeral expenses to a minimum.

As chairman of the burial committee my father was kept quite busy, especially on Sundays, his one day off from work. As the membership became older and frailer, members and their wives began dying in greater numbers.

T: How old was your father when he took on this assignment?

K: About 55, I think. Here he is working six days a week and on Sundays at least two or three times a month he is traipsing off to funeral services and ministering to grieving families. I can still remember how he would get up late on Sundays, shave, shower, sprinkle on some cheap cologne, put on a starchy white dress shirt and tie, and head for the cemetery. Usually, he'd saunter back in early enough for us to go to Mulberry Street for a bargain-priced but delicious Chinese dinner. It wasn't long before my mother began to complain about his "gallivanting" around at funerals. She often remarked, with sage perspicacity in my view, that Dad was having more fun attending funerals than he was at home hanging out with his family. In moments of exasperation she would chide him with one of her favorite clichés: "Harry, when are you going to realize that charity begins at home?" Since Dad worked late hours during the week, his moonlighting at graveside as a Sunday aide-de-camp of the Grim Reaper meant that I saw little of him during my teens. By the time he came home late at night I was either asleep or doing my homework. In time he and I had come to accept the fact that we were two bypassing acquaintances who happened to eat together once in a while, exchange short pleasantries or sarcasms—depending on the current emotional climate of the household—and sleep under the same roof.

One day I was stunned into thinking that might change. Dad told me that his nephew, my cousin Arnold, Uncle Bernie's son, would take us for a plane ride next Sunday. I had never flown in a plane nor had any of my friends, as far as I knew. Arnold had a pilot's license and flew small planes out of an airport located in Central Jersey, about an hour's distance from Newark. Each day for the rest of the week I spouted effusive declamations to classmates and friends about the upcoming aeronautical spectacular in which I was to star. By the third day most of them must have become jaded with me because I could find fewer and fewer willing listeners who would tolerate my boastful ranting. I could hardly wait for Sunday.

On Sunday, Uncle Bernie came by to pick up my father and me. We got to the airport on time and Arnold was waiting for us, pilot's helmet in hand. Arnold announced that he was allotted only an hour and a half's flying time and that he had requisitioned a small plane, a "three-seater," that could, at most, take up only two of us at a time. A quick confab between Uncle Bernie and my father produced a decision that Uncle Bernie would take the first flight with his son while Dad and I would go up together on the next flight. I watched Arnold and Uncle Bernie climb into the cockpit of the plane, put on their helmets and goggles, wave to us, and take off, and as the plane soared from the runway like a graceful bird and made its way into a cloudless empyrean, I felt the thrill of one who would soon fulfill a lifelong dream to fly in an airplane, although, admittedly, my life was not yet an especially long one at the time.

Arnold's plane soon flew out of sight, leaving Dad and me to while away our time scanning the sky for its return. Meanwhile I kept a steadfast eye on the airport clock and knew that about 40 minutes had elapsed when Arnold and Uncle Bernie were at last back on the ground. Uncle Bernie sauntered over with a big smile and immediately related all he had seen while aloft—highlighting the skyscrapers of Newark and New York, including the Empire State Building—which, as you might expect, served to further whet my imagination and urge to jump into that plane and get going. Then Arnold made a comment that I intuited to have ominous overtones. He said, "I just learned from the airport office that I have to switch to a smaller plane, a two-seater. So, Uncle Harry, I can take only one of you up on the next flight. It's either you or Sheldon. And I don't know how much time I'll have left for a third flight. I've just used about half of my allotted time." My father didn't hesitate for an instant. Without looking at or speaking to me, he took Uncle's Bernie's helmet and goggles and said to Arnold, "Let's go."

The plane took off and again disappeared into a vast, glorious sky and soon became a distant speck. They returned in approximately 30 minutes. My father got off the plane and immediately began regaling my uncle with delicious descriptions of the loop-the-loops and aerial cartwheels that Arnold executed in order to frighten and amuse him. While he spoke he ignored me and to this day I don't believe it was because he was at all embarrassed over displacing me on that airplane. It soon became clear to me that he had actually forgotten that I forfeited my seat to him and that I probably would never fly that day. That "probably" was quickly changed to "definitely" when Arnold declared, quite matter-of-factly, that his flying time had elapsed and he needed to return the plane to its hanger.

When we got back into the car, neither Uncle Bernie nor my father said anything to me about my annulled flight. Neither thought it necessary to either console or apologize to me for my crushing disappointment. Instead, adding salt to an already badly inflamed wound, they, the two co-conspirators of my misery, spent the entire trip back to Newark exchanging jolly recollections of what they had seen from the high altitudes above metropolitan New Jersey. I recall sitting in the back seat of the car wondering why God, if there was such a celestial personage, assigned Cantor Baum to torment me in Hebrew School and a father to negate my very being with his unbridled selfishness. What was I that day, Dr. Taub, a mere nugatory appendage of him, there only to make him feel that he was doing his fatherly duty by promising me a plane ride, taking me to the airport, and then not caring that I was the odd child out who must silently tolerate such callous and dismissive neglect?

T: I'm afraid so. Of course, if the second plane was a "three-seater" you would most likely have gotten your ride. But that doesn't change the fact that your father was blind to the dreams and hopes you had nourished for so long. As you have said, the disappointment must have been crushing. Your father allowed his own excitement over flying in the plane to completely nullify his interest in you that day. Once again you suffered a severe form of emotional abandonment at his hands.

K: You know, Dr. Taub, your use of the word "excitement" in relation to my father reminds me of something that happened when I was about 15. I think it's worth relating.

As I entered my teens, my interest in sex and prurient materials grew boundlessly. In junior high school pornographic Archie comic books were circulated and lustfully savored by practically all the boys. These comic books depicted Archie with a seven-foot phallus screwing Veronica atop tables, swinging chandeliers, chimneys, bicycles, and even occasionally an ordinary bed. Although the drawings were inartistic and the dialogue, which floated in bubble captions, mostly consisted of strange ejaculatory grunts and babblings, little imaginative effort was required to achieve arousal from Archie and Veronica's bizarre fornications.

One day, while browsing in a used bookstore in downtown Newark, I came upon Henry Miller's *Tropic of Capricorn* lying face-up in a box of discounted books. Knowing nothing about Miller or the book, I picked it up and perused it in an alcove for almost an hour. I used an appreciable portion of my allowance to purchase it and when I got home I hid this rich repository of prurience in a dark, undiscoverable corner of my bedroom closet. I later learned that *Tropic* had been banned and censored in the United States, so someone, perhaps a GI stationed in Europe, where it was not banned or censored, had most likely smuggled the lewd contraband into the States.

Until I had come upon *Tropic*, I had read only one other adult book in its entirety: a biography of Babe Ruth. I devoured all of *Tropic*, a longish book, in just two days, despite having reread some particularly lascivious passages many times. Especially enrapturing, if memory serves me correctly, were the sultry passages which described the blind girl and the piano teacher. Little did I know that there was more and much better to come. And, to my delight, the next sexual treat was not long in coming.

For a number of years we had owned an eight-millimeter movie projector. My father, who was an avid sports fan, had amassed a small but very good collection of college football films highlighting the likes of such great stars as Army's Doc Blanchard and Glenn Davis, "Mr. Inside" and "Mr. Outside," as they were famously known. Many a dull evening was enlivened by dipping into this collection and watching those soundless movies for a few hours.

One such evening happened to be the night of my mother's mah jong group. My mother and her friends played mah jong regularly at each other's homes on a rotational basis. As I'm sure you know, Dr. Taub, the game of mah jong was as popular as gin rummy or canasta among Jewish women on the East Coast. On this particular evening it was my mother's turn to play hostess to the group and, thus being left to entertain myself, I naturally resorted once again to joining the greats of football's yesteryears. The films lay in a bureau drawer in my parents' bedroom. My father was out playing cards with his buddies—my parents usually synchronized their game nights—so I didn't bother to ask anyone's permission to rummage through the bureau drawer in their bedroom. After discarding a few of the movie reels I had viewed overmuch, I came across a reel that was unlabeled and unfamiliar to me. Presuming this to be another football film, but one that was relatively newly acquired and not viewed before, I took it to my bedroom and eagerly placed it on the projector, flicked off the lights, and sat back with rapt attention to watch Glenn and Doc outsmart and outrun the defense.

Instead of football players and pom-pom girls, the film, a quite grainy one, opened up with three people, two women and a man, standing side by side in a nondescript living room. They mutely chatted and joked clumsily with each other for about a minute, but since the film had no captions these carryings-on soon became quite tedious and pointless. I looked closely at the three faces that flickered upon the bedroom wall, thinking that these merrymakers might be relatives or friends of my family who gathered together to make a home movie. As I inched forward to get a closer view of their features, however, one of the women reached across the screen, zipped down the man's fly and deftly extricated his penis. This sleight of hand was achieved with such skill, aplomb, and rapidity that at first I simply couldn't assimilate what had actually happened. Next, without hesitation or ceremony, the threesome proceeded to undress and, lickety-split, form a human triangle on the floor. There, amidst an undulating jumble of writhing arms and legs, they commenced a long orgy of sucking, licking, panting, and grinding which finally ended when each of the three enjoyed (or feigned enjoying for the camera) libertine fulfillment in convulsive orgasms. As the last few feet of film spun off the reel, one of the women proudly waved the man's flaccid penis toward the camera as if she were using a flimsy semaphore to send out a genial greeting to her viewing audience.

I was spellbound, ecstatic, and yet acutely frightened by my cinematic discovery. At the very time of my watching the film my mother and her friends were playing mah jong in the kitchen, which was only about 10 feet from my closed bedroom door. I could clearly hear the sound of the clicking and clacking mah jong tiles and an occasional utterance of delight or disappointment from one of the players. My mother rarely barged into my room without permission, but it was not beyond the realm of possibility that she might unexpectedly open the door to ask me an exigent question or to remind me to get to sleep at a reasonable hour. So I replayed the film several times with my finger resting at the switch of the projector. Providentially, I managed to get through three viewings without being interrupted or caught at my private pornographic premier.

Having gained access to this film posed several problems. I had no idea why my father took the chance of storing the pornographic film in his dresser drawer with the sports films. I knew that I would quickly form a strong addiction to the film, but I also understood that each time I removed and viewed it I had to be absolutely sure that I returned it to exactly the same place and position in which I had found it. And, of course, I was never to be caught viewing the film by either parent or all hell would break loose.

These scruples notwithstanding, I was exultant over my pornographic treasure trove. For one thing, the film had enormous value as a regular source of sensual excitement and pleasure. Even more importantly, however, I immediately anticipated that the film would catapult me to significant heights of esteem and popularity among my neighborhood friends. As I soon learned, my rakish anticipations were not disappointed.

Sheldon's sizzling movie became an overnight hit on Hunterdon Street. Droves of eager teenagers, some of whom I had never seen before or hardly knew, were calling me or coming to my home to ask permission, of course well out of earshot of my mother, for personal viewings. I admitted everyone, usually in groups of three or four, without charge and reveled in the riotous whooping and caterwauling of my guests. During the hours when my mother was safely out shopping or visiting relatives, my bedroom theater ran continuous performances for some highly appreciative assemblages. After about a week of this hot-blooded excitement, however, both the performances as well as my exciting, meteoric rise to celebrity status in the neighborhood came to an abrupt end, largely as a result of my own thick-witted gullibility.

In attendance at one of the showings was a black acquaintance of mine named Marshall, who lived in the large corner house at the intersection of Waverly Avenue and Bergen Street. I had first met Marshall when one day, while strolling down the 18th Avenue hill toward my home, I felt a stinging pain in my right buttocks. I instinctively reeled around and, to my surprise, saw only one person behind me, a thin black kid standing approximately 30 yards away and carrying an elongated box. Resuming my stroll, I took no more than two steps before I felt another bee-sting pain, this time in the left buttocks. Swirling about, I noticed that the kid with the box was chuckling and gesticulating in my direction.

Considering the hilarity and gesturing to be somehow connected to the source of my pain, I strode over to him to inquire about what he knew about the matter. He introduced himself simply as Marshall, which I assumed to be his last name. In an extraordinarily congenial and unapologetic manner he slid open his box, which, to my astonishment, contained a shiny, new BB gun. His guiltless, guileless way of explaining how he had just used the gun to bulls-eye my ass completely dispossessed me of my anger. Although we never became close friends, many times afterward we together looked back fondly and gratefully upon the day we met, the day when Marshall peppered my backside with BBs.

Since we had been on such good terms with each other, I was rather pleased when one day Marshall unexpectedly invited himself to my home to see the by-then illustrious movie. He had never before been in my home and I, therefore, assumed that his ill-disguised uneasiness stemmed from an unfamiliarity with his strange surroundings. The thought had also crossed my mind that perhaps he had never before paid a social visit to a white person's home and his tension was, at least in part, racial. This was a plausible explanation since at that time it was certainly true that few, if any, white families in my neighborhood ever invited blacks into their homes for any purpose other than to perform menial housekeeping tasks.

Soon after Marshall and I had viewed the film and I had placed it securely back in its case, the primary reason for Marshall's restiveness came to light. As I stepped aside to give him room to leave, he said, "Sheldon, that's one fuckin' picture. What you say if you just let me borrow it for a couple of hours?" I replied, "Come on, Marshall. This movie belongs to my father. I can't let you have it." "Shit, man," he retorted "I just want to borrow it for tonight and bring it back tomorrow. I swear." "Hell, no, Marshall. I'd be up shit's creek if anything happened to that movie. If you want, you can come back here and see it some more." "Look, man, I told you, I'm not gonna do nothin' to your movie. Let me have it for tonight and tomorrow morning I'll give it back."

Well, this verbal tug-of-war went on for about 15 minutes with Marshall gradually gaining the upper hand as he calculatingly whittled away my trust in my mistrust of him. With one last valiant try I attempted to close the matter by raising my voice and putting some finality into my objections. Marshall, however, only became more plaintive and persistent, implying all the while that, by denying his wishes, I was guilty of some unforgivable injustice to him. His pleadings finally dislodged my misgivings as well as my better judgment and, with strict instructions to return the film the following morning, I handed it over.

Marshall, as I had suspected, did not show up in the morning. Later in the day I spotted him crossing Bergen Street and when I called to him he pretended not to hear me. I finally overtook him near the 17th Avenue corner.

"Marshall, where the hell is my film? You were supposed to return it this morning."

"Sorry, man. A bad thing turned up. My father found it and he won't give it back."

"Your father did what?" I screamed.

"Take it easy, man. I'm sorry, but my father's got it."

"Look, Marshall, stop shitting me. You've got to get that film back. It belongs to my father."

"I told you, man, my father's got it and he won't give it back."

"Did you ask him?"

"Yeh, I asked him."

"Well, what did he say?"

"He said he won't give it back."

"What else did he say?"

"Nothin'."

"Marshall, you've got to ask him again."

"No, man, he won't listen to me. You ask him, if you want to."

"You think he'd give it back if I asked him?"

"I don't know. You could try."

We arranged for me to meet Marshall's father at their home after his dinner that evening. After Marshall let me in, he led me up a long darkened stairway to an upstairs room of the most spacious house I had even been in. The long trek up the stairs and the pervasive duskiness of the house added to my dread and made every step of the way seem hideously ominous.

Marshall ushered me into a large, high-ceilinged bedroom in which a middle-aged black man sat near the opposite wall. At first I couldn't find him in the gloaming of the room, but he spoke first and his features became more visible as my eyes grew accustomed to the dark.

"You Sheldon?" were his first words.

"Uh, huh."

"What you want?"

"I came for my film."

"What film?"

"The film I loaned Marshall. He said you have it."

"Oh, that film. Yeh, well, son, you know you shouldn't have no films like that. A young boy like you."

"It's not my film. It belongs to my father and I need it back."

"Well, that's too bad, son."

"Aren't you going to give it back?"

"I can't, son. Don't' you understand? That kind of film ain't no good for a young kid like you. And suppose your parents found out that you look at movies like that? What you think they would say? I think it's better if I hold onto it for you. Sorry, son."

He was in complete command of the situation and when he hinted that he could tell my parents about the film, I lost all hope of retrieving it. I went home in utter despair and wretchedly sequestered myself in my room for the night. The next few days were spent anguishing over how my life was in dire jeopardy. My father would find out what I had done and disown me. My parents would be profoundly shamed and aggrieved over my actions. I was now, more than ever, certain that I would be placed for adoption with those South Jersey farmers. I slept poorly and had great difficulty eating or keeping food down.

My parents noticed the change. The night after my meeting with Marshall senior we went out to our favorite Chinese restaurant on Mulberry Street. As always, I ordered my favorite dish, egg foo young. After making my way through about half of one of their delicious pancakes, I became nauseated and lost my appetite. My parents were amazed that I couldn't finish my favorite dish, but I blamed it on simply not feeling well. Fortunately, they probed no further.

The following evening, after giving a few cursory thoughts to resolving my quandary by doing away with myself, I had a resounding brainstorm. Somewhere in the labyrinths of my tortured mind, the simple idea occurred to me that no one could possibly find out about my misdeed unless, of course, I disclosed it myself. My parents had no knowledge of what happened. Marshall and his father would surely not report having stolen a film that they wanted to keep. My friends were loyal and furthermore were not about to reveal to an adult that they had taken part in a pornographic escapade.

But what about my father? He was the stumbling block. But was he? What could he do, realistically? Not much. Could he come home from work and inquire of my mother and me, "Hey, anyone around here come across a pornographic movie?" Hardly.

I understood that if I remained calm and completely noncommittal I might come out of this mess rather unscathed. I even began to yearn for the day my father would pipe up about the film so that I could enact my plan. Sure enough, a few weeks later I heard my father riffling through a dresser drawer in his bedroom. A few minutes later I heard him bellow out, "Has anyone here seen a missing film?" My mother ingenuously replied that she hadn't, but Sheldon might know something about it since he had often shown football movies on the projector. Now came the moment I had alternately dreaded and welcomed for weeks.

My father asked, "Sheldon, have you seen a missing film of mine?"

"A film, Dad?"

"Yeah, a film."

"What kind of film? You mean a football film? Those films are still in the drawer."

"No, not a football film."

"What did it look like? What's it about?"

"Never mind. Maybe I'll find it later."

Obviously crestfallen and worried, my father went back to his room to resume his frantic search. In less that one minute of conversation with him, I was taken entirely off the hook. Although I naturally felt great relief, I took no particular pride or pleasure in my deceit and craftiness. To this day I feel twinges of guilt whenever I think of having caused my father such distress. I've also sometimes wondered how he ultimately explained the conundrum of the missing porno film to himself. Oh, my goodness, Dr. Taub, I've overrun my time. I'm very sorry.

T: I had sufficient time today to extend our session a few minutes, but we do have to stop now. Perhaps in a subsequent session you might tell me how the discovery that your father was in possession of a pornographic movie, which he obviously viewed, like yourself, with erotic intent and pleasure, affected your feelings toward him.

K: I'd like to pursue that myself. Thank you.

Professor Kittleman's Diary 7/10/06

Diary, I must admit that I felt exhilarated after this session. I had no idea that my feelings about having my long-coveted ride in my cousin's airplane stolen by father had irked me with such intensity. My father's obliviousness to my hopes and dreams on that fateful day is almost beyond belief and yet his actions were quite characteristic of how he usually treated me. Although I spent many hours after the session in bereavement over my long-lost plane ride, I somehow managed to settle into a calmer mood by realizing that my father generally took little interest in attending to my basic emotional needs. Sure, he could boast to his friends and relatives about having a son who did well in school and stayed out of trouble in the neighborhood, but for him I had no real or singular identity as a person with delicate feelings and vulnerabilities. Hell, how could he grasp this simple fact? His own father treated him worse than one of his stable horses.

As for the pornographic movie, I've shared that vignette with my wife and a few of my closest friends. But this is the first time anyone ever asked me how my discovery of that film affected or altered my opinions and feelings about my father. Of course it sometimes takes a psychotherapist to ask a novel and penetrating question. I will give the matter some thought before our next session.

Dr. Taub's Anamnesis 7/7/06

The patient first related an episode from adolescence that graphically illustrated his father's self-indulgence at his, the patient's, expense. The patient was deprived of an opportunity to take his first plane ride because his father elected to take his place in the plane while evidently being aware of the fact that, by doing so, his son would not fly that day due to limitations of time. The patient, who had repeatedly rhapsodized to his friends about the thrilling plane ride he would take with his pilot cousin, was relegated to the role of a hapless spectator that day and, to make matters worse, his deep disappointment and despair went entirely unnoticed by his father, who was too intoxicated with his own excitement over flying in a plane to take any notice of his son's crushing emotional setback. This episode had undoubtedly left the patient feeling great rage and distrust toward his father, emotions that were clearly evinced by him throughout the telling of this painful experience.

The second half of this session comprised an episode that took place in his early teens involving the patient's finding by happenstance a pornographic movie amidst his father's football reels in a dresser drawer. As might be expected in the case of a callow adolescent, he quickly became obsessed with the movie itself and with the prestige and celebrity he garnered from his neighborhood peers as its owner and projectionist. His instantaneous fame came to a crashing demise when the film was misappropriated by the father of a neighborhood acquaintance. The loss of this film had posed a short-term crisis in his life because he thought it would be detected by his parents. Since it wasn't, he came away from this experience, from all appearances, rather unscathed psychologically. There remains the question of how he felt about his father after finding a pornographic film in his possession, a matter which we will take up at a later time.

Eleventh Session 7/13/06

K: Dr. Taub, you inquired about my feelings toward my father after discovering that he owned, and no doubt viewed, the pornographic film I found in his dresser drawer.

T: Yes. Did you wish to elaborate on that subject?

K: I think it's worth a few thoughts and comments. First of all, I was not one of those kids who believed that his parents were paragons of asexuality who suffered a single dissolute lapse on the day of his conception. Nor did I ever believe that I, like a certain well-known Son of God, had miraculously issued from my mother's womb by dint of parthenogenesis. My father constantly told jokes in mixed company, most of which were patently ribald. Whenever I was within earshot of one of those jokes, he would shield me from its meaning and dirtiest words by deftly and conspiratorially translating whole phrases into Yiddish. He evidently told these jokes well, almost always drawing loud guffaws from his amused listeners. So I knew inferentially that dad liked the honest-to-goodness carnality of sex. I might add, parenthetically, that my bedroom was quite a distance from theirs so that I was never privy to their late-night shenanigans and I don't remember ever thinking of snooping on them from outside their door.

So I think I can candidly say that learning that my father watched pornographic movies did not markedly affect the way I thought or felt about him one way or the other. If anything, I think this discovery tended to humanize him in my eyes; in other words, I found it reassuring to know that my father was as sentient and licentious a person as I was at the time. That commonality with him was, I recall, a small comfort to me whenever he and I had conflicts, which happened quite often. I should mention, however, that it was my mother who tended to be Puritanical when it came to sexual matters.

T: How, exactly, was she Puritanical?

K: My mother's prudishness could be quite far-reaching and the cause of excruciatingly awkward moments. One day, when I was perhaps 11 years old, she tried to relate a story about my raging appetite as an infant. The tale began innocently enough with a drive in the country. The tranquility of the countryside was shrilly broken when I awoke from a nap wailing to be fed. At this point in the narrative my mother hesitated, and then, beet-colored, puzzlingly fled on to end the story by mumbling something about getting out of the car to feed me. Mystified by the lack of detail and my mother's flustered posturing, I persisted a bit.

"Mom, I don't understand. Why did you get out of the car to feed me? Didn't you already have milk in the car?"

Reddening even more, my mother stammered, "You were very hungry, so you had to be fed right away."

Undaunted by this non sequitur, I replied, "Yeah, I know. But why in the woods? You could have given me a bottle in the car, couldn't you?"

"Uh, you couldn't, I didn't, well, uh, I didn't feed you with a bottle." Wheeling about, she hurriedly left the room without further ado.

It was several hours before I deciphered the meaning of her words. It took much longer for me to understand why I was not supposed to learn from her that I was breast-fed. Evidently, breasts were parts of the anatomy that could not be discussed with children, at least without exposing them to sordid and harmful notions. This, I'm sure, was the main reason why I was so upset about the lost pornographic film. Given the strict censoriousness of my mother, who held that breast-feeding was an unmentionable subject, there was truly little possibility that she might regard my access to a pornographic film with anything close to equanimity.

T: So you felt trapped between your mother's sexual Puritanism and your father's gross inability to respect and ally himself with your feelings. That is why you panicked when the film was stolen from you. You would have to explain yourself to them as you stood in the fierce crossfire of their reproaches.

K: I think that about sums it up.

T: But let me ask you, were there times when you felt that either parent really came through for you? I ask that question, not of course to whitewash the ways in which you felt emotionally neglected by them, but to gain a clearer picture of what actually went on during your youth.

K: Let me think about this for a while and I'm sure I will recall something particularly relevant to your question. Okay. Soon after I had turned 14,

I was kidnapped. Since I was not physically harmed, held hostage, or killed, and my father was not a national hero like Lindbergh, the event was not bannered in the newspapers.

At the time of my kidnapping I had spent most of my afternoons and early evenings playing basketball and swimming at the Jewish Community Center (colloquially called the "Y"), which was located right next door to the synagogue where I attended Hebrew School and was bar mitzvahed. Cattycorner from the "Y" was the Jewish Home for the Aged. Those three Jewish institutions—the "Y," the synagogue, and the home for the aged—had slowly become cultural anachronisms in this once predominantly Jewish but now largely black neighborhood. They were soon to relocate in the suburbs where, by the mid-'50s, many of their Jewish patrons had already preceded them in rapidly increasing numbers.

The "Y" was a large, homely building that exuded the strong, blended and, to my olfactory sensibilities, not unpleasant odors of chlorine, sweat, and the cooked hot dogs served in the upstairs luncheonette. The "Y" was a home-away-from-home for me during my early teens. Its swimming pool, gymnasium, teen activities and good, dedicated social workers made the "Y" a social and recreational haven for me and many others like me. Each day, as soon as I came home from school I would hurriedly pack my athletic equipment into a duffle bag and hop a 5 Kinney bus which took me to the "Y" in about 15 minutes. Usually I'd be the first one into an empty, chilly gym, which gave me daily opportunities to invent imaginary one-on-one basketball games against the greatest stars in the land, contests which I invariably won by one point as time elapsed on the clock ("Take that, Mikan"). Later in the afternoon other boys my age strolled in and half-court, pick-up basketball games were organized. Teams were usually selected by first shooting foul shots. The first players to make their foul shots were pitted against those who did not. Twenty points decided these matches and, if there were extra players, they warmed a bench until the game was over and then played the winning team.

By about six o'clock most of the teenagers had gone home for the evening. I took a half-hour break with a quick shower and a nosh at the luncheonette, a treat that usually consisted of two delicious kosher frankfurters and a Coke. By six-thirty I was back on the floor of the basketball court. For the next two hours I played basketball with the men, who had come directly from work to the "Y." Mostly in their 20s and 30s, these guys played hard but good-naturedly. Some remained in good shape since their high school years; others showed beginning signs of physical decrepitude with their barrel-bellies and frequent shortness of breath. Since I could dribble well, had good speed and threw a pretty accurate jump shot, I was easily accepted into these games and at times was even considered a highly coveted teammate.

Once off the court and back in the locker room I was of course largely ignored by the men, who kibitzed easily with one another about their jobs, cars, and women. It was enough for me to listen and to be patted on the back at the end of the evening by one of them who would puff me up with an avuncular compliment like, "Nice playing, Sheldon. See you tomorrow."

Over a period of many months the staff as well as other members of the "Y" took note of my long, daily stints in the gym and this at times was the cause of some light teasing from them. Unfortunately, it was also the principal cause of my kidnapping. One evening I decided to go home for dinner with my friends rather than stay on to play ball with the men. As we mounted the stairs leading to the luncheonette, one of my friends jokingly mentioned that we were being followed by two men who had also just left the gym. We glanced back and saw two large, burly men, one of whom I recognized as a regular of the weight lifting room, coming up the stairs behind us. My friends and I merely giggled over and dismissed the bizarre idea that we were being trailed.

Once in the luncheonette, we decided to sit down for brief refreshment. The two men also sat down and after a few minutes one of my friends called attention to the fact that they were peering over in our direction while holding a whispered conversation behind carefully cupped hands. Although we found their stalking manner a bit disconcerting, my friends and I left the building without further thought of the weight lifters.

Just beyond the exit of the "Y," however, I heard my name being called by an unfamiliar, disembodied voice. As I turned around, the two weight lifters sidled up to me, both smiling broadly and oleaginously.

"Sheldon, can we have a word with you?" the dark, hirsute one asked.

"What about?" I replied, wondering how he knew my name since we had never before spoken with each other.

"C'mon over here so we can talk about it."

He motioned to an area just outside the next-door parking lot. I separated from my friends and agreeably joined the two men in front of the parking lot.

"Sheldon, we want to know what you did with my pair of shoes." Again, it was the hairy hulk that spoke.

"Your shoes? What shoes?"

"I had a brand-new pair of shoes stolen from my locker yesterday. I think you took them."

"I don't know anything about your shoes." I didn't.

"Well, we think you do."

"Why do you think I took them? Anybody can steal a pair of shoes from a locker."

"We checked around. We found out that you were the last one to leave the locker room while we were in the shower. Your name kept coming up when we checked around."

"I don't care what anybody said. I didn't take your lousy shoes."

"Well, I think we'll need to have this investigated. So, why don't you come along with us? We have a policeman friend who lives in Elizabeth. Let's go, we'll talk it over with him and get it straightened out."

"I'm not going anywhere with you guys."

I turned away from them to return to my friends who had remained steadfastly waiting for me in front of the "Y." As I stepped away, my right arm was suddenly grabbed from behind and thrust up my back until my hand almost touched the shoulder blades. The weight lifter who had remained strangely silent until now was suddenly displaying remarkable physical prowess by contorting my arm as easily as a baker twists limp dough. When I could no longer endure the pain, I shouted to my friends, who had seemingly been bemused by my ordeal, asking them to let my parents know that I would be late for dinner.

My arm was released and the three of us walked abreast to a car in the far corner of the parking lot. I was shoved onto the front seat alongside the arm twister who was designated to drive us to the city of Elizabeth. The hirsute one took the back seat. For several miles we drove slowly in the direction of Elizabeth while both men chatted aimlessly about how their friend, Joe the cop, would cleverly solve the mystery of the stolen shoes. Every so often one or the other would ply me with a question about my role in stealing the shoes, but I remained adamant in my denials of the theft.

After about an hour the circuitous drive and the lackluster and brainless conversation about police officer Joe began to unnerve me. By then it had become painfully obvious that there was no Joe, no cop, and perhaps no escape from this mad odyssey until or unless I confessed to stealing the shoes. It quickly occurred to me, however, that such a false confession was wrought with serious pitfalls. If I caused those two nutty galoots to believe that I was indeed the shoes thief, it was possible that they might take immediate and unbridled revenge against me. Might even kill me, I thought. At the very least, a self-incriminating confession of that kind would make it necessary for me to either produce the stolen shoes or pay for them afterward. No, a confession was definitely not the way out of their pasty web. My thoughts soon fell upon the idea of a surprise escape. Each time we stopped at a red light I considered leaping from the car and running for it. Oddly, they took no special precautions against that possibility. I gave up the idea, however, when I pictured being caught by those two bruisers, who would naturally think my elopement to be a certain acknowledgment of my guilt. To round out the picture, I saw them pulling me into an alleyway, beating me to a pulp and leaving me there for the rats. No, I'd better use my head to outsmart these dullards.

"Okay. I didn't take your shoes, but I know who did," I volunteered.

Both men perked up immediately. "Yeah, who?" inquired the dark, hairy one.

"It was a friend of mine, George Gorziak. He was with me last night and took them from your locker. I saw him." The name, George Gorziak (I still remember it), was crudely and resourcefully invented as it spilled out of my mouth.

"Good. Now we're getting somewhere. We knew you knew something about it, even if you didn't take them yourself. Where does he live, this George Gorziak?"

"On Central Avenue." At least there really was a Central Avenue in Newark.

"What number?"

"I think it's 1170, but I can make sure after I get home and let you know. I should be getting home. It's pretty late."

"It's good you told us. Thanks. We'll take you home now."

"I live at…"

He cut me off by saying, "Never mind, we know where you live."

They sure did. Without a word of instruction from me they drove directly to my doorstep and dropped me off. I was warned not to tell George Gorziak that he was being sought by them. I faithfully promised not to betray them since I was quite sure that the mythical George Gorziak would be none the worse for my betraying him.

When I came into the house my mother and father were having dinner. It was disheartening to think that I would have to break the bad news to them, right in the middle of such a pleasant meal, that I had just been kidnapped. And from the estimable Jewish Community Center no less! I sat down and remained glumly silent for a while. During the first lull in the conversation I spotted an opening.

"I was at the 'Y' and I just got brought home by these two guys. They thought I had taken their shoes. I didn't, but they thought I did." No one paid particular attention.

"So I told them I didn't take their shoes but they didn't believe me. That's why they took me in their car."

My father distractedly asked me what I was talking about. My mother seemed more intent upon eating her dinner.

"I was forced to get into their car because they thought I stole their shoes. This one guy twisted my arm and made me go with them for a ride until I told them the truth. I didn't take their shoes but I made up a story that a friend of mine took them so they would let me go."

As if I had just finely orchestrated their senses and had found the right instigative chord, my parents' eyes widened with alarm and in the following brouhaha I was bombarded with questions from both sides, mainly directed at establishing if it was true that what I had been incoherently trying to say was that I had just been kidnapped.

My father jumped up from the table and went to the phone to call the police and within 10 minutes he and I were inside the lobby of the "Y." There we were met by the police who were apprised of our reasons for needing their assistance. In tandem the police, my father, and I wended our way through the halls of the "Y," entered the gym and ascended the spiral staircase leading to the circular track and the weight lifting room on the top floor of the building. As expected, my kidnappers had unwisely gone back to the "Y" and when our motley contingent entered the room they were already pumping iron. It was strange seeing such smug and cocky men wilt so quickly in the face of a direct and threatening challenge to their power and virility. The police assumed responsibility for interrogating them. With bloodless faces and quaking voices they tried to justify their criminal conduct. As I watched them shudder and disintegrate under the barrage of a very hostile interrogation I almost felt sorry for them.

At one point, the hairy one desperately blurted out, "We just wanted to scare the kid to get back my shoes. We weren't going to hurt him." That comment seemed to detonate an explosive device inside my father, who walked over to the perpetrator, stuck an index finger into his face and said, "Okay. You wanted to scare my son. Now we're going to scare you. We're going to press charges against you in court." I can tell you, Dr. Taub, it was a wonderfully triumphant experience seeing my father stand up to that muscle-bound palooka who, without question, could have benched-pressed my much smaller father 20 times without exerting himself.

We never pressed formal charges against my kidnappers. I never knew why my father did not carry through on his threat. When I returned to school the next day, word had gotten around that I had been kidnapped, which placed me in an eldritch limelight for a day or two since no one, including myself, was quite sure whether being kidnapped was something a person should feel proud or ashamed of.

There's not much of an epilogue to this zany tale. I saw the two men many times afterward at the "Y." Even when we were alone together in the weight lifting room, we never exchanged anything more than wary glances at each other. Quite a few years later I learned that the dark, hairy man was a remote relative of my wife's sister through marriage. I suppose that makes him some kind of distant relative of mine, an oddity that does not, I can assure you, lift my spirits.

T: We're going to have to stop soon, but I first wanted to inquire about your feelings toward your father when he stood up to the kidnapper in the weight lifting room.

K: It was one of those rare times when I thought that he really cared about me. Of course it didn't entail a great physical or moral risk for my father to stand up to those brutes while he was standing side by side with two hefty police officers that were packing guns in their holsters. Nevertheless, I felt that his voice, when he made his threat of criminal prosecution, carried a tone of conviction and rage that reflected his deep love for me and his realization that I had been unjustly imperiled and violated by those two scumbags. Much to his credit, he never questioned me about the missing shoes, apparently correctly convinced that I was completely incapable of such knavery.

T: It's unfortunate, isn't it, that it took a perilous situation such as your being kidnapped in order for your father to proclaim his love for you. This was the second time within just a couple of years when you had reason to believe that your life was in mortal danger—the other of course being the time when the mob of rock-carrying kids came after you. Those two experiences must have left you feeling a deep sense of emotional and physical vulnerability. However, it must have been reassuring and comforting to know that your father, at least on this one occasion, desired to be your protector and guardian; in short, your good-enough, dependable father, when you most needed him.

K: I suppose so, but when I used the word "imperil" it brought other thoughts about him to mind; times when he seemed to place my safety and welfare in his mental garbage can. I'd like to talk about that next time.

T: Of course. Take care.

K: You too.

Diary, this last session, which was largely about my kidnapping at the "Y," engendered a surge of rage in me that has remained unabated ever since. What the fuck did those two animals think they were doing when they took me on their sham expedition? They not only scared me to death but afterward I never quite felt entirely safe and secure at the "Y" and up to that time the "Y" had always been a haven, a refuge to which I would go each day to escape the irksome vicissitudes in my life. Perhaps the worst violation was that of being robbed of that wonderful refuge and that I resent the most. You know, I have felt so pissed off that I had a fleeting fantasy of contacting my sister-in-law, getting from her the hairy one's address, visiting him at home and surprising him with a belt in the snout. This, after 50 years! Evidently, some vengeful feelings never die. Well, for all I know, he's dead and my wish for revenge has outlived him. I hope so, and I hope his was a most painful death. Sorry, diary, but that's how I feel—at least right now.

As for Dr. Taub, he's a great listener but I feel that he prematurely and too often looks for silver linings in my befouled cloak of childhood experiences; as when he played up how my father championed me to my kidnappers in the weight lifting room—supposedly out of love. It may very well be true—perhaps it was, as Dr. Taub contends, an effusion of love on my father's part when he went to bat for me in the weight lifting room—but I derive little solace from that possibility given Dad's many acts of indifference to my emotional and physical welfare.

Is it any wonder that I have homicidal thoughts about Dr. Taub? He must be the very embodiment of all the base men who tyrannized and humiliated me in my youth—my father, Cantor Baum, Uncle Bernie, Marshall's father, and the kidnappers. Does the fact that I know I am a woeful victim of my own wild displacements and a grand negative transference make me less homicidal? I don't think so, diary.

Dr. Taub's Anamnesis 7/14/06

The patient has had more than his share of harrowing experiences during childhood, engendering in him a profound sense of emotional and physical fragility. A kidnapping experience deprived him of the full pleasures and safe rewards of recreating at a local Jewish community center, a facility he had frequented as a youth. Although his father acted quickly and affirmatively to protect and defend him in this crisis, the patient is quite intransigent in his denunciations of his father who, according to the patient, more often than not betrayed him emotionally. Are these denunciations warranted and proportionate? It's hard to judge but I believe they are tinged with a good degree of distortion and exaggeration.

Although there is considerable evidence of the presence of a positive transference thus far, the fact that the patient continues to verbally monopolize our sessions and mostly relates to me as if I were an incorporeal self-object suggests, I believe, a rather high degree of narcissism. He manifests one of the classic hallmarks of narcissism—the contempt for and devaluation of others—by curbing, through his tale-telling monologues, my participation and importance in these sessions. I must guard against colluding with and thereby reinforcing his defense of devaluation by remaining overly passive while at the same time allowing him the freedom to tell his life's story in the manner that suits him best; that is, as he would put it, as an inveterate contextualist. In other words, I must harness my countertransferential (narcissistic?) wishes to be actively and recognizably important in these sessions in order to avoid injuring and alienating the patient's already fragile sense of self.

K: I realize that, in our last session, I was obstinately holding onto my negative opinions of my father as you sought to inject hopeful signs of his love for me. I know I'm a cantankerous and defensive patient but I cannot, at least for the present, be receptive to your attempts to balance or amend my hostility for my father with tiny analgesic time capsules that contain rare memories of feeling loved by him. Au contraire, I feel compelled to tell you much more about what I didn't like about my father and his unfatherly ways.

T: Before you do, I wanted to ask if you thought I was perhaps being Pollyannaish or dismissive of your angry feelings for your father by citing an instance when he might have been displaying his love for you. Perhaps you may have even felt that, by identifying his actions as an emblem of his love for you I was allying myself with him against you. In other words, you may have interpreted my comments to mean that I thought you were being too critical of him since he may have loved you after all. If you did interpret my remarks in that way, you had reason, I think, to be very angry with me.

K: It's a bit of a relief to hear you say that, Dr. Taub. Yes, I did feel that you were trying to sugarcoat the unpleasant truth about my hateful feelings toward my father. And, yes, it did feel like you were siding with him against me. It was almost as if I could hear him, through you, saying, "You dare to criticize and hate me. Don't you know that I loved you? You're an ungrateful, contemptible son." And, yes again, I have felt angry with you since our last session because I felt misunderstood by you.

T: And how did being angry with me affect you?

K: To be truthful (what else can I be here?), I felt somewhat unsafe with my anger.

T: In what sense?

K: I had this irrational fear that my anger would jeopardize our relationship. I'm not sure how. I suppose I imagined that you would be angry with me for being angry with you and you would then retaliate in some way. I know this is a fear I always felt around my father who had little tolerance for the anger of others, although he was enormously tolerant of his own nasty temper. This discussion brings me back to some of the things I wanted to tell you today, if you don't mind.

T: You're certain that you are not avoiding telling me more about your anger toward me by switching the subject to your father?

K: Perhaps I am, but I do feel you need to know more about my father in order to appreciate the depths of my anger for him. I'll take your silence as a "go-ahead" sign. I've already told you that during my teens my father was a proprietor of a dry cleaning establishment.

Ordinarily, very little of his business entailed over-the-counter transactions in his shop. It was the door-to-door delivery service that was the lifeblood of the business.

Dad usually made two daytime deliveries each day, one in the morning and one in the early afternoon. His route took him through the towns of Union, Irvington, Maplewood, and then, on his way home at night, he made a third series of home-deliveries in Newark. His van, which was a large box-shaped jalopy, was used for his daytime house calls. At dusk, after closing up the shop, we drove home in his laggard, road-untrustworthy Ford in which we hung customers' clothes onto a long dowel that was suspended crosswise from just above the rear windows. These were the clothes my father dropped off to his customers on our homeward journey and it was this nightly transit through the streets of Newark that I found so farcical and incensing.

T: Why was that?

K: Well, let me start with my father's theatrical performances.

T: Theatrical performances? I didn't know he had performed in the theater.

K: You take me a bit too literally, Dr. Taub. My father didn't need a theater in order to be giddily theatrical. Although he had never read Shakespeare, he knew the world was a stage, his stage, and he especially enjoyed performing on our rides through the streets of Newark.

T: I don't understand. How could he do that from behind the wheel of a moving vehicle?

K: Dr. Taub, your inquiries are timely and incisive, most relevant to my tale, and are therefore deeply appreciated. As we would drive down a city street my father would espy someone he knew, not necessarily well, but that didn't matter. He would roll down the window, take his eyes completely off the road for a few seconds, and yell out "Hymie, Moise, Sammy, or Jake," or whatever the hell the unsuspecting person's name happened to be. Almost always, the individual whose name was called out would turn around and look in our direction but, nine times out of 10, the guy obviously did not know who it was that was shouting his name from our car. But, then, that was not the point.

T: What was the point, then?

K: The point was to let me and himself know that he was a very important person, known by multitudes of his landsmen as an important, eminently recognizable, personage in the Jewish section of Newark; at the risk, I should point out, of having us both killed.

T: How so?

K: Well, I mentioned that he had taken his eyes off the road each time he called out to an acquaintance. Each time he did I riveted my eyes on the street in front of us and readied myself for a catastrophic accident. I surely expected a car or a person would pass in front of us just as my father was putting some high bravura into his street performance. Providentially, this never happened, but the rides home were always harrowing because of his crazy vaudevillian antics behind the wheel.

T: So it was these dangerous narcissistic performances behind the wheel that incensed you so much?

K: Dr. Taub, that was only the half of it.

T: What was the other half?

K: The other half was much worse. When we did home deliveries in the winter the evening temperatures were often well below freezing. The erratic heater in the car worked most of the time, so the ride was usually reasonably comfortable. However, there were several delivery stops along the way so that meant turning off the car and the heater. I was never asked by my father to join him in delivering the clothes to customers so I stoically sat in the teeth-chattering cold and dark of the car until he returned. I can assure you, Dr. Taub, my father rarely returned quickly from these sojourns of his. On the contrary, he usually took his time—20 minutes to a half hour or more—to complete each delivery. Throughout the interminable waiting I sullenly ruminated over what could possibly detain him for so goddamn long. When he finally returned, he never seemed to take note of the fact that I was shivering and silent with rage as we took off for our next destination. One night, sorely oppressed by being made to languish in the freezing temperatures of a brutal storm for almost an hour, I took matters into my own hands and decided to solve and, if possible, end the mystery of my father's extended acts of decampment.

I left the car and ascended the stairs where I had seen my father enter an hour before. It was not long before I heard his voice on a landing one flight above me. He was kibitzing with his customer, a woman who intermittently laughed over my father's witty caricatures of some of the people in their neighborhood. It was apparent that my father was not attempting to propitiate this woman in order to collar her as a customer. Rather, he was regaling her like a vaudevillian who simply covets the laughter and applause of his audience. But my father had, in the process, completely forgotten he had a son freezing his ass off in the car.

I didn't want to cut into my father's performance, not because my stealthy eavesdropping provided me with titillation or amusement in the least, but because I knew he would heartily disapprove of any intrusion on his tour de force. At last, realizing that he was just catching his second wind with a joke of questionable taste, I let out a loud, feigned cough that caught his attention. Interrupting his joke, he looked down into the staircase where he managed to spot me in the dim light. I could discern his familiar angry frown even in the distant darkness. "Well, what is it?" he asked. "Dad, it's late and I'm cold." "You're cold? Go back in the car. It's warmer there." "Dad, that's why I came inside. It's freezing in the car. I want to go home." Evidently, the woman standing in the upstairs doorway was moved by the plaintive tone of my voice because she said, "Harry, I think you had better go. It's not good for your son to be so cold. He could get sick."

Evidently, my father, who otherwise was clueless about the severe damage that could be done to a young boy by prolonged exposure to freezing temperatures, had to be cajoled into an act of humanity toward me by a simple, commonsensical word of kindness from a person who had not even set eyes on me. He broke off his lollygagging and took me home. Amazing, fucking amazing.

T: And the ride home? How did that go?

K: The same as it usually went. I sat in stony silence the entire trip home while he nattered away about the wonderful, classy lady he had just left. Not once did he detect that my silence was both my shield and my sword. I hated him and wished him dead and gone.

T: His obtuseness and blindness to genuine dangers to your health were inhumane and infuriating.

K: "Genuine dangers to my health." That phrase is apt and ignites a couple of other charming memories about my unbelievable, life-endangering father. May I?

T: Please.

K: When I was 18 my father and mother were staying at a *kochalyn* in the Catskills—you know, one of those small hotels where you cooked your own meals—not far from where I was working as a camp counselor. I called over to the hotel and asked my father to lend me the car that night; I needed it to go out with a girl who worked at another camp, a young houri who favored the supine position and, to my way of thinking, the back seat of my father's car seemed like the ideal venue to accommodate her sexual proclivities. I hitched a ride to the hotel from a camp friend. When I got there my folks were having dinner and my father just handed me the car keys without saying a word or missing a bite. I gave myself plenty of time to spare so that I could reach the camp at an early hour, bed, or should I say "back-seat" the girl, and then get back to my camp before the ten-thirty curfew. The car was an oldish but serviceable Pontiac and I swiftly scudded along the dark country roads with only delicious thoughts of unwonted carnality on my mind. Then it happened. On one of the darkest stretches of road I had yet encountered a gunshot-like explosion detonated from the rear of the car and I was suddenly riding on the left rear rim where a tire had been only seconds before. I gradually maneuvered the car to the shoulder of the road and, since I couldn't see a thing, I semaphored SOS pleas for help by frantically waving my arms at passing drivers.

Either I was not seen in the dense darkness or drivers were wary of stopping for this ostensibly berserk roadside madman, but it was a full hour before someone—the eventide Samaritan, I now call him—pulled over and offered to help me. I told him I had borrowed the car and didn't know where all the tools were. With the benefit of his own battery-run lamp, a lug wrench, a jack, and a rare spirit of altruism, he replaced my tire with one taken from the trunk and I was on my way. Before he left, though, he said in a tone of admonishment that whoever lent me that car was reckless beyond belief; all the tires, including the spare, were completely bald. It was a wonder, he said, that the others had lasted as long as they did. By the time I got to my destination, my date had given up on me and had gone back to her cabin. I barely made it back to my camp before curfew. So, what began as a sojourn into a night of carnal bliss ended in near-catastrophe and some after-curfew onanism.

T: This experience, as you describe it, has the hallmarks of a classic psychoanalytic theme; a father who wants to kill his son, remove him from the Oedipal triangle, by having him drive on bald tires in the middle of the night. As well, it is likely, I think, that your father understood that you were going to use the car for *shtupping* purposes that night and, as your rival in the triangle, he wished to thwart your having sexual conquests in his car, even if it meant going to the extreme of exposing you to great physical dangers. What do you think of that interpretation?

K: Plausible, Dr. Taub, but much too glib and, in my view, way off the mark, at least when it comes to the matter of my father having active death wishes for me.

T: Why?

K: First of all, my oblivious father drove on those selfsame tires himself. Was he trying to kill himself, too? Hardly. You know, a week later camp ended and I spent a few days with my parents at the hotel. Ignoring the fact that the car had dangerously bald tires, I nevertheless borrowed it so I might go into town to catch a movie. I suppose I figured the Grim Reaper wouldn't have time to nab me on such a short drive. I got to town easily enough, saw a movie, got back into the car, turned on the ignition and then the lights. At least I thought I had. I pulled on that light switch a dozen times but the recalcitrant headlights remained dark and dumb to my manual entreaties. It was late evening, my parents were no doubt asleep and there were no open gas stations in that small mountain village. The best I could do was to get the parking lights to work and then I took off for the hotel. Thinking I had idiotically forgotten to turn on the headlights, oncoming drivers, one after another, blared their horns at me as I perilously snailed my way along that dark county highway, constantly keeping a sharp eye out for the narrow turnoff to the hotel. Miraculously, I found it and made my way back to the by-then-darkened hotel.

The next morning I told my father what had happened and why. His reply: "Oh, I forgot to tell you. The headlights don't work unless you jiggle the switch close to where it comes out." No apology and no sense of horror over what calamity his shameless oversight might have caused me. No, Dr. Taub, I don't believe my father's colossal neglect that night or on the night of the flat tire incident reflected a death wish he had been harboring toward me. Rather, it was something far worse than wishing me dead. It was, I believe, an indifference to whether I was alive or dead. It simply didn't matter to the man whether I existed on this planet or not. His mind was elsewhere—on himself, mostly.

T: I'm sorry, but we have to stop now.

K: I'm sorry as well. I feel as if I'm close to some deeper discovery about myself. See you.

Death wish, my ass. I only wish my father had wished me dead. That would have meant that at least he sometimes thought about me; that I was to him some mortal, perishable, sensate entity that lived, breathed, thought, felt, and might die as a result of a car accident caused by a faulty light switch or bald tires. Instead, I was to him a cipher, a discardable inconsequentiality, not worth a whole lot more than the snotty handkerchiefs he dry-cleaned in his shop.

Dr. Taub was undoubtedly right, though, when he pointed out that Dad's shenanigans whenever he lent me his car—for example, his infuriating tendency to ignore or deflect my attempts to pin him down to a specific time for taking it out on a date—were a product of his warm rivalry with me, spawned most likely by his own sexual frustrations over a lifetime, and particularly heightened whenever he imagined that I would be using his car for what Dr. Taub so aptly called "shtupping purposes." Having a Jewish therapist clearly has its advantages, diary, especially when a Yiddish word like shtoop ono-matopoeically gives rich color and sound to the act of sexual inter-course better than any English word I can think of.

Now what am I to do about my feelings toward Dr. Taub? Yes, diary, these sessions that have revived memories and feelings about my father have intensified my anger, not just in the form of posthu-mous patricide (if there is such a thing, even in one's imagination), but toward my old man's handy surrogate, my therapist. I've never before actively felt like killing another person and therefore I've never been faced with having to tell anyone that, by the way, "I think I may kill you." How do I break the news to Dr. Taub without unduly frightening him and destroying the hard-won benefits of many weeks of productive therapy? Will he opt to involuntarily lock me up in some psych ward under the authority of a state statute or simply tell me, "It was nice knowing you, but I think it best that you find another therapist, preferably one who has a bodyguard, wears a bulletproof vest, and has an office in some distant city?" I've always prided my-self on my moral courage and now I must, goddamnit, enlist some of it in order to be fully candid with Dr. Taub about my heinous secret. My irrational self tells me he must die but my reasoning powers tell me he deserves a far better fate and is at least entitled to an honest proclamation from me about my demented designs upon his life.

A most interesting session. Professor Kittleman described gross acts of remission on his father's part that truly endangered his life, yet refutes my conjecture that his father's dangerous acts of neglect stemmed from (most likely unconscious) wishes to kill him because he viewed him as a sexual rival for his wife, the patient's mother, and for the young women the patient dated. Is the patient rejecting my interpretation because he can't face his own homicidal thoughts about his father, or is he perhaps correct in believing that his father's narcissism was so severe that he couldn't help but completely devalue his son's very being to the point of patrimonial negation, and therefore it was natural and easy for his father to expose him to life-threatening situations? After all, logic would suggest that a person who utterly lacks importance in the mind of another individual will be viewed as undeserving of protection from even the most lethal of dangers.

There is no question that the patient's unresolved feelings about a decidedly disappointing father are crucial to him and to his treatment, but I sense that the topic of his father has become something of a hobbyhorse used to avoid discussing other highly important relationships from his past, such as his marital relationship. I think I will point that out to him in our next session and see where it takes us.

K: Dr Taub, I think it best for me to begin this session by telling you that I have for about the last six weeks been pussyfooting around a matter that has been a source of great concern and apprehension to me And I think it is high time that I…

T: Excuse me for interrupting, Dr. Kittleman, but I think it necessary for me at this juncture to preempt you with my own thoughts about a few matters. I hope you don't mind, but may I continue?

K: No, go right ahead. I mean no, I don't mind, of course. Please continue. I may mind later, but I suppose that will depend on what is contained in your preemption.

T: Well, here it is. I believe our therapy is going very well. You are obviously using our sessions quite productively and there is every reason to believe that you will continue to do so. I've observed, however, that our recent sessions have been almost entirely devoted to your memories and feelings regarding your father. I am not suggesting that this sharp focus on your father is either disproportionate or without therapeutic value. On the contrary, considering the depth of your emotions about him and the clearly traceable connections between your painful experiences with him throughout your youth and your later struggles with feelings of personal insignificance and vulnerability, I would say that we have far from exhausted the fertile field of your powerful memories about him.

K: So why leave the "fertile field" now? Is there a greener, more fecund field germinating bountiful crops of emotion just outside the compass of my conscious mind? If so, please tell me where it is and I'll get on your trusty tractor and the two of us can together plow our way over there posthaste.

T: Okay. Here's my thought. It is common in therapy for patients to become intensely focused upon and preoccupied with a particular person or set of experiences in their sessions not only to uproot and resolve important emotional conflicts, but sometimes to avoid intense feelings about other important people and experiences that have affected them deeply. I've been wondering whether this might now apply to you.

K: Who and what do you suspect I've been avoiding?

T: Your wife, for one, Dr. Kittleman. After all, she was the most important person in your life for many years and yet you've hardly spoken about her to me.

K: Perfectly true, Dr. Taub, but I can't say for sure that I have been shunning the prospect of talking about her in my sessions. I have from time to time given thought to telling you about her but, since I haven't considered my most serious personal problems to have been rooted or reflected in my marital relationship in any particular way, I thought I would delay discussing my wife, Ethel, with you. I have no objection to broaching the subject of my marriage, however, if you think it would be helpful.

T: I think it very well might be helpful in that it would give both of us a deeper understanding of your emotional life throughout your adult years.

K: I'm not sure where to start. Ethel and I grew up in different sections of the same city. Her neighborhood was largely Jewish and mine was ethnically diverse. We first met at a dance held in the gymnasium of her high school. I went with a friend—each of us seeking to meet a Jewish girl—and we spent the early part of the evening eyeballing the girls aligned along the wall on the other side of the gym. When we finally honed in on two especially prepossessing "chicks," as we then called pretty girls, they were coquettishly panning the boys assembled near the bleachers with lustrous, wistful eyes. My friend arbitrarily chose the one on the left and I quite willingly beelined my way to the one on the right. These proved to be quite fortuitous, compatible pairings and each couple stayed together for the remainder of the evening.

That evening also proved to be fateful for Ethel and me. My friend, Fred, enjoyed the evening, dated the girl one time and never saw her again. Ethel and I, on the other hand, dated off and on until I graduated from high school and went on to the local university in downtown Newark. We saw little of each other for well over a year and then, when Ethel graduated high school two years later and enrolled at the same university, we began dating again, but this time more seriously and monogamously.

Ethel wanted to get married while we were in college. I was hell-bent on taking a moratorium from academic studies and from our relationship upon graduation from undergraduate school by escaping to Europe on a vagabondish summer vacation. I somehow felt I owed it to myself after having my nose strapped to the academic grindstone for four years. It was a selfish, foolhardy thing to do, leaving poor Ethel behind like that, wondering, no doubt, whether I might come back home with another paramour or, perhaps, not at all.

I shortened my vacation by about a month and, tail between my legs, surprised Ethel with my unheralded appearance on her doorstep, announcing my heartfelt intentions to marry her as soon as our respective families could arrange a wedding. She didn't hesitate a moment and bore no discernible grudge over my pain-inflicting desertion. The wedding was relatively small and modest, much in accordance with our taste, and we left immediately afterward on a New England honeymoon.

The earliest years of our marriage were halcyon in all respects. Ethel finished up undergraduate school with a major in education and immediately found a position in a Newark high school, mostly teaching history and English. I went on to graduate school for a Ph.D. in clinical psychology and with her earnings as a teacher and my stipend as a teaching assistant, we were able to easily make ends meet and even afford to go out to dinner and a movie a few times a month to boot.

After a few years, however, a cloud of uncertainty and concern cast a dark shadow over our marriage: Ethel could not conceive a child despite our best efforts and the sage advice of medical experts. We were finally informed that Ethel suffered from an inoperable gynecological anomaly that stemmed from a childhood accident and entirely obviated fertility. If having children was an imperative in our lives, we should, the doctor opined, consider adoption as a viable and potentially life-fulfilling option. We were both deeply disappointed of course, but our feelings and opinions about adoption at once diverged and clashed sharply and acrimoniously over this matter. It was then that I disgraced myself by hurting Ethel, the person I loved the most.

T: How? What do you mean? How did you disgrace yourself?

K: By steadfastly refusing to adopt children under any circumstances. Ethel had few qualms about adopting kids. She wisely advised that we go about the adoption process in a gradual, thorough, and painstaking way and ultimately adopt only if we both genuinely agreed the child under consideration was a suitable match. None of her eminently reasonable, generous suggestions carried any weight with me, however. I was obdurate and since I was completely irrational on this subject, poor Ethel must have felt like she was trying to reason with a tyrant and a madman. For a short time I thought she might leave me and go off to find another man, someone with the decency not to deny and rob her of her lifelong hopes to be a mother as well as a wife.

In time Ethel ceased to exhort me with droll images of exuberant kids romping about the house, learning to read and play musical instruments, laughing over my corny jokes, and greeting me with hugs and kisses when I came home from work. She swallowed her pride and resentment by acceding to my tyrannical selfishness and made the most of our childless marriage.

We of course enjoyed and fulfilled ourselves in myriad ways. Ethel was an excellent teacher and easily won the affection and respect of her students and colleagues. I immersed myself in my work and gradually gained widespread recognition for my authorship of some influential writings on the subject of college student conduct issues. It was this corpus of publications that eventually catapulted me onto the lecture circuit and ultimately led to my recent disgraceful downfall.

Of course Ethel contrived as best she could to heal the cavernous void I had savagely carved out of her life. But how could she or anyone else in her position accomplish such a thing even within an entire lifetime? Believe me, I had constantly tried to make it up to her with untold acts of genuine kindness and consideration. She was appreciative and gracious always despite the fact that she fully understood that I had scorned and repulsed her fondest emotional hopes and cravings. But we both knew that, henceforth, nothing I could do would ever truly make up for the hurt I had inflicted upon her. What more can I say, Dr. Taub?

T: Quite a bit more, I think. Significantly, you have not attempted to explain why you resisted the prospect of adopting children with so much obduracy despite Ethel's zealous attempts to sweeten the pie with positive, realistic portrayals of what parenthood would be like for the two of you.

K: I would have thought you would have guessed, Dr. Taub.

T: Guessed what?

K: Why I stubbornly vetoed the adoption idea.

T: You're being coy and hesitant to tell me and evidently want me to guess. Are you perhaps baiting me for some reason?

K: I suppose I wanted you to know without my telling you. Well, here it is in a nutshell: narcissism, again rearing its ugly head.

T: I'm afraid that, without any elaboration, your comment about narcissism explains very little.

K: It's like this. Along with millions of other people, I needed and required that my children be my biological heirs; in other words, any child of mine had to be consanguineously yoked to me, not to some stranger with a completely different genetic makeup. I wanted—rather, I insisted—that my children must have some of my inherited characteristics, even those I didn't particularly like or admire. As long as they were mine, it didn't matter. I steadfastly and misguidedly believed that I simply could never love a child who was conceived during an act of lovemaking by anyone other than Ethel and me.

Of course my everyday experiences belied this belief since I enjoyed and felt great affection for many of the children I met in my personal and professional lives. Yet I could not rend the clutch of those emotions that compelled me to want offspring that were nothing more or less than my genetic doppelgangers; not vibrant, reasonably autonomous children with unique and endearing personalities but kids who would bear, first and foremost, a corporeal (however imperfect) resemblance to me, their egoistic progenitor. So, Dr. Taub, that is why Ethel and I remained childless and that is why I brutishly insisted on having my way.

T: Did you not consider that you might, just from a selfish point of view, have gained more from having someone else's children than from having none at all?

K: Many times. But, once again my narcissism won out.

T: How so?

K: I had to experience triumph.

T: Over what or whom?

K: Over the biological parents, of course. If they could procreate and I could not, I was not about to humiliate myself by adopting their child. That, to my way of thinking, would have been a crushing emotional blow. If they had the biological capacity to have a child and yet chose not to keep and raise it, why should I, who lacked these awesome advantages, make life easy for them by providing the kid with a wholesome upbringing? I can tell from the dolorous expression on your face, Dr. Taub, that you consider my remarks to be the epitome of feckless, egomaniacal triumphalism, and you are right. Are you, now that you know who I really am, thoroughly disgusted with me?

T: What makes you think that?

K: Along with the telltale expression of horror on your face, I would say that you, a demonstrably compassionate, altruistic man, must be appalled by me, the self-indulgent reprobate. I behave as if I care about people but I make the most important decisions in my life based almost entirely upon my selfish needs.

T: If that is so, it doesn't make you disgusting. Rather, it makes you tragic in a profound sense. After all, by depriving your wife and yourself of children, you and Ethel most likely lost untold opportunities for cheer and fulfillment that would have strengthened and enriched your marriage. Is that not so?

K: It is so. May I take one of these Kleenexes? Thank you. You have recognized my tragedy. It is interesting that one of our foremost psycho-analysts—I know you know who I mean –made the profound observation that narcissistic persons are not especially conflicted in the Freudian sense, that is, overcome by guilty conflict-ridden struggles with their naughty instinctual urges, but rather are tragic human beings because their impaired sense of self cripples their ability to enjoy life to the fullest. Tragedy in the theater usually implies, I was once taught by a professor of drama, a personal collapse from great heights such as the elevated stature of a leader or king. In my case, I'm afraid I collapsed and languished well before I ever reached the stature of prosaic mediocrity.

T: Are you now indulging in self-flagellation?

K: Perhaps. I know our time is nearly up so I'll just say that—and I can never get this out of my mind—Ethel and I had a good, loving life together. But it could have been better, much better, if I had not been such a selfish blockhead. When she was being buried at the cemetery I was suffused with an instantaneous mad urge to leap into her grave to tell her that, had she not died so suddenly and prematurely, I would have found a way to have children with her, adoption or no adoption. But I knew even then that I was making a bogus imaginary gesture at giving her a posthumous gift, one that I could never fulfill had she lived. You and I know that, given our age at the time of her death and my twisted psychological makeup, my urge at graveside was nonsensical, a grotesque lie, but no matter what happens in here from now on, I will never forgive myself for what I didn't do for her.

T: That feeling of remorse, Dr. Kittleman, strongly suggests that you are not the selfish scoundrel you believe you are. We do have to stop now. I did preempt you at the beginning of the session but would encourage you to return to the issue you were about to discuss today when we meet next, if you'd like.

Diary, can you believe it? I finally girded my loins, or whatever it is that one girds when mustering up courage, to confess my murderous ruminations and I'm preempted by the good doctor who omnisciently discovered that I have been caching dark secrets about my marriage in the attic of my unconscious. Maybe it was, as he said, a form of self-flagellation to refer to myself as a mediocrity but I am ashamed of my stubborn refusal to bless poor Ethel with children to love and nurture. So, if I need a few minutes of self-flagellation to expiate my guilt for the harm I did to Ethel, so be it. Like those old-time Catholics who donned hair shirts, I'll take some forms of self-flagellation over a mountain of guilt any day.

But why did he have to interrupt me at the very moment when I was disclosing my macabre secret? Did he somehow intuit that I was on the verge of declaring that I wished to kill him and, out of fear, decide to interdict my declaration? Is he that omniscient? It's a funny thing, diary, this business of omniscience. Like most patients, I suppose, I sometimes wish Dr. Taub had the powers of omniscience. I would sit silently and indolently in his office, he would clairvoyantly read my thoughts and I would feel very special for being so exquisitely understood. But isn't there a dark side to this wish? I would have no secrets, no privacy, and virtually no autonomy of thought. Dr. Taub would then become my puppeteer. Now that I think of it, this is precisely the problem with paranoiacs. Their narcissistic wish to have their every thought understood and appreciated leads them to believe that their feelings and emotions are transparent. This belief causes them to feel highly vulnerable and subject to the control and machinations of others. Thus, they construct their conspiratorial and persecutory conceptions as a way of dealing with their fragile vulnerability—in other words, "It's the other guy who's doing bad things to me; I'm not the source of the problem." I feel touches of this sort of paranoia when I'm in Dr. Taub's office but so far I think I'm containing it within a safe boundary. I hope I can tell Dr. Taub my secret without losing my balance and sanity.

Dr. Taub's Anamnesis 7/30/06

I'm not certain whether I did the therapeutically correct or necessary thing when I diverted the patient from his chosen agenda at the beginning of the hour. Perhaps I did that because I had grown weary of allowing him to call most of the shots when it comes to the matter of what we discuss. I know this is a common problem for therapists who work with highly narcissistic patients. After a time we begin to feel dismissed, devalued, and worthless. Although I know the patient induces such feelings in me because he himself is struggling with deep feelings of insignificance, it is sometimes difficult for me to feel enough empathy for someone who views and treats me like a sounding board most of the time. Or am I, like the patient, simply flagellating myself. Perhaps this last session was of some value after all in that it encouraged Professor Kittleman to more deeply discuss an important facet of his life and personality—the need to have only offspring who would be mirror images of himself, even at the expense of depriving his wife and himself of having children altogether. Of greater importance, I believe, is the fact that this session, like no other, enabled him to express his profound grief, regret, and guilt over denying his beloved wife unparalleled opportunities to love and be loved by her own, albeit adopted, children.

K: I don't know where to begin today. I, uh, don't feel much like talking, if you want to know the truth. Perhaps you could jump-start me, Dr Taub, since I'm feeling a little like one of my father's broken down jalopies.

T: There's a tone of annoyance in your voice. Perhaps your mood relates to our last session; you know, when I interrupted you in the middle of your opening remarks. Is it possible that you're hesitant to speak for fear that I'll once again cut you off?

K: Perhaps. Twain observed that a cat that sits on a hot stove would not sit on one again; nor will he sit on a cold one. Maybe I still haven't figured out whether it's completely safe to speak my mind today. How can I tell? What's the litmus test for something like this?

T: Perhaps you might start by telling me how you felt when I sideswiped you in our last session.

K: I don't know exactly. Perhaps sideswipe is too strong a term. I understood that your intentions were just and honorable; you wanted to help me unearth some long-buried feelings I had about my wife and our marriage. I suppose I could feel angry about being interrupted, but those feelings get trumped by a logical realization that I'm not, as Freud might put it, always traveling on the royal road to my unconscious. And you could very well know, better than I at times, in what direction we should be traveling.

T: It's interesting, I think, that when I asked you about how you felt about my sideswiping you, you not only tried to tamp down the strength of my word but then shielded me from your anger by attributing honorable intentions to my intrusion on your train of thought.

K: What else could I think? Weren't your intentions honorable and trustworthy when you interrupted me?

T: Yes, they were. But that's not my point.

K: What, then, is your point?

T: My point is that it sometimes matters very little what my or anyone else's intentions are when you have an emotional experience, such as took place in our last session, that feels negating. And I believe that is how you felt when I interrupted you. I believe that you felt negated and angered by me and haven't allowed yourself the emotional freedom to accept or acknowledge those angry feelings, to me or even, perhaps, to yourself.

K: How do you know that?

T: I can't say I know it in the pure, scientific sense. But I have good reason to believe you have been very angry with me based upon your behavior and my feelings at the outset of this session. Let me explain. Unlike any previous session, you began by faltering and then announcing that you had nothing to talk about. In this way you conveyed your distrust of me. You thought I might once again preempt you and this was an expedient way of avoiding that possibility. It points to the anger you must have felt over my interruption last week.

K: You also mentioned your feelings as a clue to identifying mine.

T: Yes, I was about to come to that. I felt rebuffed and rejected by you and I didn't like that. I felt depreciated by you. I recognized my feelings as reflecting your hostility for me. There is one more thing I would like to mention, however. While you were struggling with your angry feelings you mentioned something about my honorable intentions.

K: What about that?

T: You recall I'm sure how often your mother, whenever she or you had cause to be angry with someone, would proclaim that the culprit had, after all, meant well. I think you were doing the same thing when you quickly attributed honorable intentions to me, even though I slighted you with my interruption. This enabled you, as it did your mother, to avoid and deny your anger, which must have somehow felt dangerous or lethal to you at the time.

K: Dr. Taub, I can't determine if your observations and interpretations are precisely accurate and true, but I find them helpful, especially what you said a moment ago about my perceiving anger, my anger, to be a dangerous emotion. All of this brings me to where I was at the beginning of our last session, just before I was, according to you, slighted by your interruption. I'd like to continue with what I was about to say and since this cat feels less wary now about setting foot on a presumably cold stove, I'll do just that. Dr. Taub, when you interrupted me last week, I was about to tell that I have been harboring some piercingly hostile emotions toward you for some time. Perhaps calling my feelings piercingly hostile does not do justice to what I actually feel. These feelings frighten me because, even though I understand much about their provenance—for example, in my profound rage toward my father—they don't subside as a result of my discussing or becoming more aware of them in these sessions. Instead, they grow in intensity and they are almost exclusively directed at you, my anointed healer and redeemer. As you might imagine, I have been struggling unsuccessfully to tell you about my—what word should I use for my feelings? Crazy? No. Murderous? Yes, murderous. Those are the feelings I've felt toward you. When I finally found the courage to tell you my hideous secret last week, you blindsided me with an unforeseen interruption. After our session I thought I would never return to the subject. However, you, in your estimable wisdom, detected that I was angry and demoralized by your preemption, as you pointed out. And you have sensitively grasped how much anguish I have been feeling ever since. So, now, with your help, I feel emboldened to tell you what has been on my mind for so long.

T: How long?

K: Well, if you can believe this, I recall feeling homicidally toward you even before we met. I recorded it in my diary. Naturally, our many expeditions into my quirky mind have given me some insight into the origins and generators of my murderous rage, but, contrary to my expectations, none of our work together has dissipated the intensity of my feelings. I still often feel that I want to kill you. What am I saying? How can I sit here calmly and logically telling you that I want to take your life? This isn't a subject that can be dispassionately discussed between a probable killer and his intended victim. Dr. Taub, before we go any further, you've got to call the police to have me arrested, put away in a psychiatric facility for the criminally insane. Will you do that?

T: Rather than panic and resort to extreme precautionary measures, I would advise that we continue to discuss those murderous feelings you are harboring toward me. I feel confident that the more we know about them and the more we bring them out into the open, the less lethal they will feel to you and the more control you will exercise over them.

K: How do you know this, Dr. Taub? It hasn't held true yet. As I've told you, thus far, the more we have discussed my miserable life, the greater has become my anger, especially toward you, my tour guide through the murky labyrinths of my troubled past.

T: I can't precisely predict the future of our work together, but there are a couple of things in your favor.

K: Like what?

T: Well, for one, you have found the courage to share your "hideous" secret with me. You may not recognize this as a positive step, but I should tell you that it required considerable trust on your part to tell me that I am the object of your most hostile emotions and imaginings. I think that may portend well for both of us.

K: I wouldn't be too sure if I were you, Dr. Taub. First of all, I need to know something. And I want you to be completely truthful with me. What are you going through now that I have told you my dark secret? I mean, of course, emotionally. What can you tell me about your current state of mind? You've just discovered that you're sitting in your heretofore hermetically safe office with a certifiable maniac. Doesn't that revelation rattle you any? Isn't there some feeling you have, deep down, of itchy perturbation that you'd like to scratch?

T: That's a fair question but I'd prefer to delay my answer until we find out a bit more about you. Can you tell me, as best you can, why you're asking me to reveal my emotional state to you at this time? I think knowing more about what's behind your question may give me helpful clues as to how to answer your question most effectively.

K: Always the therapist, the consummate professional, Dr. Taub, searching for dynamic reasons and causes. I admire that quality in you and for that reason will do my best to adhere to your therapeutic strictures. I'll tell you why I think I need to know something about your current emotional state. It's because I'm depending on you to help me through all of my craziness, including my bizarre homicidal feelings toward you. If I have somehow destabilized you, caused you to lose your emotional equilibrium, by revealing my murderous feelings for you, then we are entrapped in a dangerous and inescapable cul-de-sac. I want to be able to safely tell you everything I think and feel, including the worst. At the same time, I want you to accept all of my deranged feelings and thoughts with emotional equanimity. Yet, if the truth be told, and I'm afraid it must, I also want you to be fearful of me. In other words, I seek the impossible from you. Why? Because, like Goldilocks, I want to crawl into that perfect therapeutic bed of yours that will not be too hard and rejecting because you fear and loathe me and or too soft because you feel the urge to magically rescue me from my deep sense of vulnerability. Am I making myself clear, Dr. Taub?

T: I think so. You wish for me to disclose information about my current emotional state in order to determine whether I am more or less human, have genuine concern for you. In other words, if my response to your lethal urges is to feel an appreciable but controllable fear—an authentic human reaction under the circumstances—and I dedicate myself to using that fear to further understand and help you, I might in time gain your trust and your pledge to do me no harm. Did I get it right?

K: The inflection in your tone strikes me as being rather sardonic but you did capture in words my thoughts exceptionally well. I realize, Dr. Taub, that I am, like most off-the-wall narcissists, asking for the near impossible in a therapeutic relationship. I also realize that I am pressuring you into walking a very thin and precarious line with me, a high-altitude tightrope that, as far as I can tell, comes with no tangible safety net beneath it to catch either of us. That is why I have to ask you if you're up to this preposterous challenge of helping me. And the best and only way I can find out is by asking you something about your emotional stability, your state of mind, ever since you stumbled upon my perverse thoughts about murdering you. What can you tell me about your mental health at this time?

T: I'll try to respond to your inquiry satisfactorily. Please let me know if anything I say is, in your estimation, amiss. To begin, I think it advisable to tell you that over the course of my career I have been faced with many situations in which my life has been threatened by my patients, in varying degrees of course. In each instance I must evaluate the gravity of the threat in order to determine when it poses an imminent danger to me or others or is largely an expressed homicidal rumination that does not represent any particular peril to me or anyone else. I should point out that in each and every instance, including the one that involves you and me, I take the threat seriously. By "seriously" I do not mean that I am alarmed or acutely concerned for my safety and welfare, but only that I recognize and appreciate the fact that when a patient harbors and expresses murderous thoughts for a therapist, or for anyone else for that matter, that patient is not only intensely angry but is in great emotional pain as well. And it is the hurt and suffering—the torment—that are the driving force of the anger. That being my premise, I endeavor to help my patients search for the roots of their suffering and rely upon that search, carried out with painstaking care and sensitivity, to heal some of the emotional wounds of the past. That, to my way of thinking, is the best antidote for dealing with overwhelmingly wrathful and vindictive emotions. Am I clear so far, Dr. Kittleman?

K; Yes. But how do you know when a patient is simply expressing innocuous homicidal ruminations—did I just spout an absurd oxymoron?—or is instead expressing murderous thoughts and intentions to kill. In other words, how do you really know whether or not the raging thoughts will bear poisonous fruit, are actually precursors and predictors of a lethal deed?

T: That, Dr. Kittleman, will have to be the subject of another session since we're out of time today.

K: But you haven't broached the subject of your mental health.

T: No, I haven't, but I promise that I will do that in our next session, if you wish.

K: I find this all very puzzling. I just told you about thoughts and feelings that are tantamount to a threat upon your life and you are calmly telling me that we will continue discussing this matter in our next session. How do you know there will be another session? You actually trust me enough to let me leave here without calling the cops and having me put away in some lockup? I find that quite bizarre.

T: See you next time, Dr. Kittleman.

Professor Kittleman's Diary 8/5/06

Diary, I must be going out of my mind. I surmounted an important barrier in therapy by telling my therapist that I have contemplated killing him and he reacts as if I had just told him his bathroom needs a new roll of toilet paper, which, by the way, it does. Now I must consider a couple of divergent but equally plausible possibilities: the man has ice-water in his veins and does not easily succumb to fanciful allusions of being killed by an elderly Jewish academic who, as a child, killed whole armies of ants but never a human being, or he is not as seasoned and savvy as he purports to be and therefore cannot recognize a good assassinative threat when he hears one.

I did my best to plumb his innermost feelings about my murderous disclosure but all I've gotten back thus far are temporizing and equivocating tactics spiced with the sweet-sounding condiments of reassurance and explanation. Diary, is he going to come through with a heartfelt disclosure of his feelings about my murderous histrionics or not? Or will he continue to prevaricate and thereby drive me to carry out the very deed I most dread? Is he going to go on cruelly tantalizing me with inauthentic, unfulfillable promises that he will be emotionally truthful with me? He'd better not, if he knows what's good for him.

Dr. Taub's Anamnesis 8/4/06

It seems that the patient has crossed an important psychological threshold in disclosing that he has for some time harbored intense wishes to kill me. Although the sudden, grisly nature of this disclosure had a disconcerting, visceral effect upon me, I believe I was outwardly calm in discussing it with him. In the course of this session I did my utmost to assess whether I was indeed in imminent danger from the patient and concluded, not with complete conviction I might add, that I could afford myself the luxury of more time and opportunity to engage him in pursuing an alleviation of his vindictive obsessions through our therapeutic work together. Since my life may depend upon it, I certainly hope my judgment in this regard is sound and reasonably prescient.

The patient is importuning me to disclose my current emotional state from the time I had learned of his homicidal ruminations. Although I am ordinarily chary about taking such a tack with my patients, I think it may be of psychological benefit to this patient for him to know that I have had the most common emotional reactions to a homicidal threat (albeit, only in the form of verbalized lethal wishes, not an actual premeditated plan to kill me). I will therefore tell him something about my dread and fear without, I hope, conveying that I am so destabilized (to use his word) that I am tempted to wash my hands of him. On the contrary, I hope to convey as forcefully as I can my determination to remain his steadfast therapist for as long as he needs me. I also hope I am not making a fatal mistake.

K: I suppose I should start by asking you, Dr. Taub, if you are now willing to share what you have felt ever since I have burdened you with the disclosure about my lethal thoughts toward you.

T: Yes, I think this is an apt time for me to do just that. To begin, your disclosure caught me completely by surprise. I could easily imagine, based on what you have told me about your hatred for your father, that through the transference that almost always develops in therapy you would from time to time feel hateful feelings for me. I tend to expect this sort of thing from patients and am usually prepared for it. When I am on the receiving end of antagonistic feelings in a session I try to grasp their meaning and use the opportunity for understanding and helping the patient. I intend, if you'll permit me, to do the same for you. However, the reason your disclosure took me aback had something to do with its abruptness and bluntness. In our sessions you are normally a gradualist who takes his time in making a point, often using an anecdote to make that point. But in our last session you were blunt and stark in announcing that you often wished to kill me. So, coming back to my emotional reactions, I was jarred and, to be even more frank, rather frightened. It seemed for a moment that you were a different person; perhaps a dangerous one with whom I was entirely unfamiliar. I then realized that for both our sakes I needed to steel myself against my fears and remain, as you yourself had observed, the professional, the ever-reliable, fittingly competent therapist. And I did that by first searching for the roots and meanings of your murderous feelings.

K: And, considering your self-acknowledged emotional state at the time, you accomplished that marvelously well, Dr. Taub.

T: Thank you. But of course my response to you was incomplete in that I had not yet divulged my feelings of fear, which, at this time, I would like to elaborate upon. I'll start by saying that therapists, like most other human beings, generally do not like hearing they are the intended quarry of another person's homicidal imaginings. And I am no exception. So I can frankly tell you that I fear you. However, I can also tell you that my fear is not at this time so acute or overbearing that I dread the thought of being your therapist for as long as you need me and for as long as I am able.

K: Two questions for you, Dr. Taub. First, why would you remain loyal to me, knowing that I am sometimes suffused with loathing and murderous thoughts for you? Second, you qualified your last comment by using the phrase "as long as I am able." What made you use that phraseology?

T: Well, to answer your first question, I recognize that your anger and loathing are only a part of who you are. You are a person who has cared deeply for others—students, colleagues, your wife, for example. You gained a renowned reputation for being a champion of civility on the college campus. And let us not ignore the fact that you have come to me for help and not, I believe, for the purpose of killing me. In short, you strike me as being a person who has embraced and evinced in the way you have lived and worked a humane set of values and ideals. I will remain loyal to you, as you put it, because I believe in you and want to support you in your struggle to overcome or at least control your hatred of me and others so that you may lead a fulfilling life, one without the great anguish with which you are presently afflicted.

K: That's reassuring, but what about the "as long as I am able" qualifier?

T: I meant by that that one can never foresee what the future, at least the distant future, holds.

K: You mean by that, I suppose, debilitating illnesses or an unavoidable relocation to another geographical area?

T: Yes.

K: I wonder if you also mean by that that you might have to prematurely terminate the treatment, drop the ax on me, because I have done or said something that arouses a deeper concern in you about your safety.

T: Such as?

K: Well, it could be anything. Such as my telling you that I have purchased a weapon, a firearm, for instance. Or that I have formulated a foolproof plan for killing you and have picked a specific date for its execution, if you'll pardon the bad play on words.

T: Are you perhaps subtly telling me that you have actually considered doing either of those things?

K: No, Dr. Taub. If it is any comfort to you, let me tell you as unsubtly as I can that I have contemplated those nefarious schemes only as hypothetical examples of what might provoke you into deep-sixing me from the deck of the good ship *Therapy*. But you haven't fully addressed my concerns. What would you do, Dr. Taub, if you or I somehow put a heavy foot on the accelerator of my rage and I suddenly reported to you that I had a well-formulated and surging plan and means for killing you?

T: I can't say for sure but I would have to follow the requirements of the law as well as the ethical codes of my profession.

K: I think I know what that means, Dr. Taub.

T: Do you? Could you please elaborate?

K: It means *Tarasoff*.

T: You are, I assume, very familiar with *Tarasoff*?

K: Of course. I have often referred to *Tarasoff* in my talks at colleges. It usually comes up when counselors want to know how to handle situations in which students confide in a counseling session a credible intention to hurt or kill an identifiable victim. The case began in 1969, in Berkeley, at the University of California. A Mr. Prosenjit Poddar, a voluntary outpatient, confided to a university psychologist his intention to kill an unnamed girl who was readily identifiable as Tatiana Tarasoff. His stated intention was to kill Tatiana when she returned home after spending a summer in Brazil. I'm sure, Dr. Taub, that you know most of the facts of this landmark case but I think it advisable for me to relate to you what I know about it so that we can join forces in evaluating how to apply the legal principles enunciated in *Tarasoff* should we one day be faced with a similar predicament here. May I further elaborate?

T: Of course.

K: Thank you. On the request of Poddar's psychotherapist, the campus police briefly detained him, but he was soon released because, according to the police, he appeared rational; he evidently promised to stay away from Tatiana. The psychologist's supervisor, who was consulted on the matter, also directed that no further action be taken to detain Poddar. Interestingly, the supervisor, a psychiatrist, by directing that no action be taken to confine Poddar, had countermanded the recommendations of two university hospital psychiatrists and the psychologist under his supervision to commit Poddar to the hospital for observation and evaluation. Most importantly, from a legal and humanitarian point of view, no one warned Ms. Tarasoff or her parents that she was imperiled by Poddar. Needless to say, when Tatiana returned from Brazil, Poddar killed her. Leaving aside some of the legal minutiae of this case, I'll just say that Tatiana's parents filed a successful lawsuit against the university alleging that it had failed to warn Tatiana's parents (and, by dint of this fateful oversight, Tatiana herself) of the impending danger and had also failed to duly confine Mr. Poddar under a state welfare and institution code. They argued that the university, by failing to take these measures, was legally responsible for her death. In other words, they argued, the failure to warn Tatiana and others who were likely to apprise her of the danger constituted, if I am quoting their argument accurately, "a breach of the therapist's duty to exercise reasonable care to protect Tatiana."

Initially, the Superior Court ruled in favor of the university, but the case was then remanded to the California Supreme Court. Although the California Supreme Court acknowledged and respected the awesome difficulty of forecasting the precise level of dangerousness of a psychiatric patient, it noted that university therapists did in fact predict Poddar would kill, but were negligent in failing to warn. They therefore ultimately ruled in favor of the plaintiffs, Mr. and Mrs. Tarasoff, judging that therapists, although they hold an obligation in most cases to maintain the confidentiality of their patients, also hold a higher obligation to protect intended, identifiable victims as well as the community at large from harm. In other words, therapists are not only expected to be competent, ethical professionals but at the same time must take cognizance of the fact that they are first and foremost citizens of a democracy that requires of its entire citizenry, including members of the psychotherapy profession, that they must act affirmatively in the public interest to prevent those who report intentions to harm or kill others from enacting their lethal threats. In the case of psychotherapists, this prevailing legal principle has, ever since Tarasoff, placed a duty upon them to take whatever reasonable measures are necessary, including the commitment of threatening patients, to protect intended victims and the public interest. That's about it, Dr. Taub.

T: An excellent summation. I can easily imagine that counselors you have spoken to at conferences have learned much essential information from you about their legal responsibilities and obligations.

K: I suppose so. But you know, Dr. Taub, I suspect that all my blabbering about the *Tarasoff* case is just a lot of fuss and feathers.

T: What makes you say that?

K: Because *Tarasoff* may have little relevance or applicability to our situation.

T: And what makes you say that?

K: Well, *Tarasoff* is a case that involves a patient who reports his intentions to kill a person the therapist does not know except, possibly, by name only. In other words, the patient does not pose any direct or imminent danger to the therapist, only to this other person, a third party. In our case, I may one day pose a direct and imminent danger to you. What, then, is your recourse? Are you going to forewarn yourself about a danger of which you are already aware? That, I think, would require some unexampled casuistry on your part and in the end afford you little protection from me. So, what other legal stratagem might you use, Dr. Taub, to deal most immediately and conclusively with what you might consider to be a genuinely dangerous threat from me?

T: I think you know what that is, Dr. Kittleman, since, I imagine, you've often had the opportunity to discuss this important stratagem, as you call it, with those counselors who have attended your college lectures. Nevertheless, I'll spell it out for you. In practically all the states in this country many mental health professionals, including myself, are vested with the legal authority to expedite procedures for the involuntary commitment of their patients to psychiatric facilities for the purpose of observation and evaluation. Usually, the maximum time for these commitments is only 72 hours unless a court order extends the period of hospitalization.

K: And what are the criteria for delivering someone to the loony bin under this statute?

T: There are several, as I'm sure you know. The patient, in the estimation of the therapist (and, I'll add parenthetically, police officers, who in most states are also vested with the authority to carry out this procedure) must be gravely disabled or a danger to self or others. In this state the statute is colloquially referred to as "5150," after its number in the handbook.

K: And you can 5150 me if you think me a danger to myself or to you?

T: That is correct.

K: But I still have a couple of questions for you, Dr. Taub. For one, at what point in my therapy might you resort to 5150 by taking reasonable measures to prevent me from harming you? Also, and this is a related question, how do you really know when a patient such as myself can be safely trusted to enter or leave your office without committing murder? What are the mighty predictive mental faculties you possess and the infallible psychological criteria you use to decree that a patient's demons finally fought their way across the Maginot Line of his fragile sanity and are now urging him on to kill? Aren't you, Dr. Taub, playing God—without of course possessing truly godlike powers—when you must make such infinitely elusive yet fateful determinations? Please tell me what you think of my questions.

T: Because I have been faced with these fateful decisions many times during the course of my career, I've had to ask myself these questions repeatedly and I have no completely satisfactory answers to them. But I will say this at the risk of appearing self-serving. I always try my best and enlist all the worthwhile knowledge I have learned and the excellent training I have received to make an imperfectly good decision while recognizing that I am fallible. There is, however, one more thing you should know. As I've said before, I have taken your non-violent history (if we can leave aside for the moment the ant army you crushed as a youth) into account along with your many years of championing the importance of civility and respect on college campuses. These personal factors, I believe, are important contraindications of a potential for violence. But in the final analysis there is something else that is enormously determinative in matters such as this.

K: What is that, Dr. Taub?

T: Well, I can't speak for other psychotherapists, but in the end I make assessments and determinations about a given patient's potential for violence by trawling through my own emotions for predictive clues. I sound my emotional state for information, about myself and about my patients, and I can only hope that the judgments I make are reasonably reliable and beneficial to my patients, including you of course. How I feel toward you can be a trusty barometer of what you are feeling toward me and vice versa.

K: And what does your present emotional state tell you about me and my emotional state, with particular reference to my potential for murdering you?

T: As best as I can tell, I feel safe with you, your many references to killing me notwithstanding.

K: Can you tell me why you feel safe with me?

T: I have come to trust you as a reflective, respectful, and ethical man who, like everyone else, has his dark, potentially dangerous, side.

K: And my dark, dangerous side is not an important part of who I am?

T: Yes it is. But let me quote from the writings of two distinguished authors to illustrate my point of view on this matter. It was claimed that Goethe said, "There is no crime, however heinous, that I could not conceive committing myself." Oscar Wilde opined, "There is no such thing as morality or immorality in thought." In other words, Dr. Kittleman, if we can find a way for you to more fully embrace, rather than condemn and disavow that dark side of your being, I believe you will be better able to drive your inner demons back across the Maginot Line of your sanity whence they can harmlessly correspond with you now and then if you wish, but at your discretion and convenience, of course.

K: Excuse me for laughing, Dr. Taub, but I find that to be a delightfully comical image. You know something, Dr. Taub; I just had a fetching thought I'd like to share with you. It seems to me that the professional psychotherapists of the world must, like me, be afflicted with a good bit of the pathology of narcissism in order to do their job capably. After all, how can they sit on their royal thrones dispensing psychological wisdom to the benighted masses without being instilled with a god-complex? You have told me that you mine your feelings in order to make awesomely crucial decisions about your patients. Who is to say that your feelings are any more barometrically reliable than the next person's as a guide to direct one to a healthy destination? To so profoundly and unreservedly believe in the guiding wisdom of one's feelings requires, I believe, an overflowing reservoir of narcissism. Perhaps, though, there are two kinds of narcissism: one that is healthy, inspiring a person to greater heights of self-betterment and positive achievement and another that leads to self-glorification, acts of grandiosity and foolishness and, ultimately, tragedy.

T: Can you give me an example of what you mean?

K: Sure. It must take a good deal of raw narcissism to cause a man or woman to aspire to be the President of the United States, indisputably the most powerful position in the world. This personality characteristic no doubt inspired Nixon to aspire to this pinnacle of the body politic but his grandiosity and thirst for power transformed him into a reprobate who thought he could, with complete impunity, rule as emperor of the country while engaging in blatant acts of criminality. Bill Clinton, one of my favorite public egoists, was certainly driven by overweening self-love to become the President of our nation but his narcissistic grandiosity and heightened sense of self-entitlement caused him to blithely believe that he could gyrate to Monica's blow jobs right there in the exalted White House without paying the price of public ignominy. What wanton chances our narcissistic leaders take! As for W…

T: I'm sorry for interrupting but our time is up. If you wish, we can continue on this subject in our next session.

K: Yes, I think I'd like that. See you then.

Diary, are these many sessions of therapy that I am reporting to you just a series of bad dreams? Can it be true that I have just been calmly and logically discussing with an interlocutor, a man I pay good bucks to be my therapist, my incessant thoughts of assassinating him at some indeterminate time in the future? Is it possible that he is actually a bedlamite, a nut, who can't get it through his thick head that I pose a mortal threat to him? Gosh, he might even be an impostor who actually came to town as a drifter, rented and furnished a nice office, bought some good clothes, stuck up a glossy shingle, and memorized a glossary of psychological terms, but doesn't even have a college degree or a modicum of psychological training. If so, his has been an inimitably convincing imposture. One other thought, diary: maybe the guy's really a serious depressive with acute suicidal tendencies. Maybe, by sticking by me, he thinks he can dupe me into killing him as a favor. That's like that old joke about the masochist and the sadist: the masochist says to the sadist, "Hit me." The sadist says, "No," thereby inflicting a sadistic no-pain punishment upon the pain-seeking masochist. Diary, why am I having all these crazy thoughts? Am I going out of my fucking, unhinged, homicidal mind? Yes, diary, I know that's a rhetorical question you can't answer. After all, you're nothing but a dumb, besmirched sheet of paper on which I write my demented thoughts.

Dr. Taub's Anamnesis 8/11/06

Matters have taken a somewhat disquieting turn in Professor Kittleman's therapy. He has disclosed to me his wish to kill me, although it seems that he has formulated no practicable scheme for enacting this wish nor has he expended any effort to procure a lethal weapon such as a gun for this purpose. Of course, such a patient needs no premeditated plan in order to carry out an act of homicide; such things can happen in a trice following a moment of impulsive and explosive rage. Also, it's obvious that one doesn't need to own a gun or a bomb in order to possess a lethal weapon. Weaponry can assume many quotidian and innocuous guises: a kitchen knife, a car, a lamp, a screwdriver, a fist, a ballpoint pen, or to use an example from an enthralling story by Dahl, a frozen steak. So why am I not taking affirmative steps to protect myself in order to prevent this man from actually killing me?

I have shared with Professor Kittleman some of my reasons for believing he will not resort to homicidal violence: there is virtually nothing in his personal history that suggests or portends that he is capable of carrying out such an act—up to now, that is. He also seems, as best as I can tell, to be in possession of an "observing ego" that is exercising reasonable judgment, including moral judgment, and is conscientiously pursuing an analytical and rational way to resolve and control his emotional conflicts, i.e., psychotherapy. I am depending largely on our therapeutic alliance to foster and stabilize an intact sense of self. This alliance is, admittedly, embryonic at this juncture of the therapy, and perhaps from the patient's point of view, entirely non-existent.

I stand ready to act more decisively if the patient gives cause. *Tarasoff*, as the patient recognizes, is not especially applicable since I, as the possible intended victim, would be required to report my patient's threats to myself, to myself, a tautological absurdity if I've ever seen one. The 5150 statute that allows me to arrange for the patient to be involuntarily taken into custody for a possible psychiatric hospitalization would likely be my first legal recourse should I deem him an imminent danger to himself or me.

We shall see.

K: Dr. Taub, if you don't mind, I'd like to further elaborate on my thoughts regarding narcissism and the presidency. As I've said, I believe that the quest for this office requires a powerful narcissistic drive on the part of the aspirant. I also believe that it is that same narcissistic drive that corrupts and derails the occupants of that office once they have had some exposure to the accoutrements of the power it wields. I was, when we concluded our last session, mentioning George W. Bush, a preeminent cartoon version of a narcissistic character run amok. This buffoon is so infatuated with himself that he has become blinded to some of the ugliest and most dangerous realities faced by humankind. For so long he did not believe there was such a thing as global warming, so he eschewed treaties that would address that problem. Then he invents spectacular lies for invading Iraq, the Saddam Hussein/9-11 connection and the weapons-of-mass-destruction premises. When those lies were exposed, he tried to justify the invasion of Iraq by packaging and selling it as a humanitarian mission: a holy crusade to topple an evil dictator. This man, who, before he became President, hardly read the newspapers and never traveled beyond the hallowed borders of his beloved country, embraced a messianic cause to transform and democratize a Middle Eastern country sorely lacking in democratic traditions. And this wondrous feat would be accomplished by exercising the might and moral authority of our government and its military forces. But, despite all the fraud and chicanery, the country reelected the son of a bitch.

T: I can understand why you are so incensed but I don't quite understand why you wish to discuss this topic with me at this time.

K: Let me spell it out, Dr. Taub. When Bush arm-twisted Colin Powell to go to the United Nations to convince the world that Saddam had weapons of mass destruction, Powell showcased the "incontrovertible" evidence of their supposed existence with a presentment of grainy photographs accompanied by an even more grainy explanatory narrative. I, for one, after looking at the photos in the newspaper at least 10 times, told practically everyone I knew that those photos would not hold up in small claims court. How could Bush and Powell believe that the world would buy such shit? But, as we know, most people in this country—including a great many liberals—and a good many others across the globe bought the whole rotten caboodle.

I will now try to make my point, Dr. Taub. My point is that narcissistic characters are not only prone to lying in order to achieve their personal goals—it's an excellent way to devalue the intelligence of others—but are often rather charismatic and convincing when they tell their lies. This enables them to marshal a large gathering of adulatory followers. I suppose Colin Powell was one of those credulous followers and, as we know, he paid for it with his reputation.

But my central point is this: narcissists, especially powerful and influential narcissists, can be a very dangerous breed of person. Their solipsistic Weltanschauung is largely a view of the world as seen from a barricaded, fragile, and blinded self and if, like Bush, they happen to control the affairs of the most powerful country in the world, we are all in a state of great peril. And we are, Dr. Taub. Take it from me, we are. I live in daily dread over where this headstrong, misguided man has taken all of us.

Just one more thing, Dr. Taub, before I leave the subject of Bush and his destructive handiwork. I have come upon the occasional speculation that Bush invaded Iraq and deposed Saddam primarily to one-up his father who, you will recall I'm sure, did not finish off the tyrant in the first Gulf War. I personally attach some credence to that conjecture. Now if we can extend that theory a bit, we might allow for the possibility that the invasion of Iraq was really an enactment of an Oedipal drama in which W was acting out an archaic childhood wish to kill his father (through a symbolic act of castrating one-upmanship in attacking Iraq) so that he would be free to fuck Barbara, symbolically of course. Now, if there is any validity to this psychobiographical claptrap I have been espousing—and I think there is, damn it—it means that one of the greatest tragedies in the history of the human race—the wanton destruction wrought by this administration upon our defenseless planet—had its genesis in Barbara's steadfast refusal to cuckold W's dad and sleep with him instead.

Anyway, in a roundabout way I am trying to make the point that narcissism can be an inspirer of good or evil deeds. I hope you will forgive my excessive obliquity, but I have rather deviously used the Bush example to illustrate how unbridled narcissism can lead to deadly consequences in order to also let you know once again that I fear my own megalomania will cause me to commit the gravest of crimes: murder. Since you are the hapless object of my worst passions, I thought I should let you know what I, in my own pathetic and meandering way, have been trying to tell you. Now, Dr. Taub, where do we go from here? How are you going to save me and yourself from personal ruination?

T: I think a good place to start is where we left off when you first announced to me your preoccupation with your murderous feelings toward me. I am suggesting an indirect but essential route to the resolution of those feelings by once again encouraging you to explore your past for memories that will generate pain and anger. It will continue to be a bumpy, difficult, and uneven journey but if you will allow me to accompany you every step of the way, I think we can together protect you from your impassioned demons and at the same time open your mind to a far better way of thinking and feeling.

K: Felicitous routes and journeys, huh? When you talk like that, Dr. Taub, I begin to feel like Dorothy skipping along the Yellow Brick Road with her chimerical pals. Am I to expect that you and I will one day, after treading many painful miles together, have an audience with a fraudulent wizard who will tell me how to live my life? Or perhaps you are that sham wizard, Dr. Taub, promising much and in the end delivering only disappointment. I'm sorry for being so twistedly cynical and sarcastic, but I am simply giving voice to my despair.

T: I understand that, Professor Kittleman. I of course can make no promises other than I will always do my best. I hope that will be good enough, at least for the time being.

K: Okay, let's forge ahead. Where shall we resume our journey?

T: I would suggest that you tell me, if you can, an earlier memory of an experience that left you with piercingly murderous feelings. I know the many times you must have felt that way toward your father, but are there any other memories that surpass those?

K: Let me think for a minute. I'm retrieving a memory that I have relived many times in my life, but always with the same unsatisfactory outcome: fury and bitterness.

T: Would you care to tell me about it now?

Professor Kittleman's Therapy

161

K: No, but I will of course. The good ship *Therapy* must sail on into ever-stormier waters if it is to reach its coveted destination, the incomparable port of Hope. So let's go back to my early adolescence, the years I attended junior high school in Newark, New Jersey. I lived in a tough but not especially violent neighborhood. Most of the families in this neighborhood led hard-pressed lives, but their kids usually stayed out of serious trouble with the law, engaging only in minor acts of delinquency and vandalism. Along with friends and classmates, I broke a few windows, regularly stole a few comic books from the rear corner of Woolworth's department store, scrawled soap-graffiti across car and house windows on Mischief Night, the evening that immediately preceded Halloween, and got into a few bloodless but mostly victorious fist fights. Some of the tougher kids joined gangs. I knew them all but never socially hung out with them; not out of fear but simply because they were uninteresting dolts and, being Jewish, I'd be an ethnic anomaly in a gang that had absolutely no Jewish members. As you know, Dr. Taub, the term Jewish gang member is largely an oxymoron, unless, of course, we're talking about gangsters like Bugsy Siegel and Meyer Cohen.

Both gangs in my neighborhood assumed bellicose names, the Romans and the Barbarians, and their bellicosity was displayed on their colorful jackets with militaristic insignia and pictorial depictions of, in the case of the Barbarians, a grotesque, marauding savage and, in the case of the Romans, an armored, battlewise warrior. Incidentally, the Barbarians came mostly from families that had emigrated from Northern or Eastern Europe and the Romans almost entirely from Italy—so the gang members were smart enough to at least get their ethnography straight. For the most part, the speech and social behavior of these punks consisted of empty bluster and ridiculous strutting, all amounting to the display of a silly pseudovirile affectation. Every once in a while we would hear about someone who had been beaten up by them but, compared to some of the drugged out, territorial city gangs of today, those Romans and Barbarians were Little Lord Fauntleroys. I vividly remember the day when one of the Barbarians picked a fight in the schoolyard with a rather husky Ukrainian kid who spoke with a marked accent and, because he tended to be a loner, had no reputation of any kind. The Ukrainian kid, who probably, as a young child, had seen and survived the horrors of war in his native country and managed to harden himself against threats to his life, fought fearlessly and well. I saw it all, from the first blow to the last. The bloodied Barbarian squealed for mercy and received it from his adversary, but not before being badly banged up and humiliated. Afterward, the Ukrainian was left alone by both gangs. Their avoidance of him seemed to come from both a respect for his pugilistic prowess as well as a creepy feeling that if he were pushed too far he might be capable of some really dangerous form of mayhem, like murder. In other words, he was suspected of being a highly dangerous, albeit reclusive, lunatic. Afterward, whenever he took his solitary walks around the schoolyard, all of us, I vividly recall, gawked at him with awe, but he never seemed to notice or care. Commensurately, the Barbarians came down a notch in the eyes of their schoolmates because the Ukrainian literally punched a large hole in the myth of their invincibility.

T: But what does all of this have to do with you?

K: Patience, Dr. Taub. I'm about to come to that. It happened that my school locker was adjacent to that of a Roman, a short, powerful, stumpy kid named Rocco. He and I, despite our occasional proximity at the lockers, never spoke or had anything to do with each other. Then, one day while I was talking with one of my pals, I backed up and accidentally bumped into Rocco. Rocco didn't waste any time. He began shoving me against my locker and then proceeded to pummel me with both fists. The blows hurt but fortunately none of them were aimed at my face. As much as I could I parried his shots to my body with my arms and although my arms were bound to ache afterward, I surely did not want to take a blow to my stomach, which is where he aimed some of his bayonet-like thrusts. He didn't stop because I had resisted his onslaught in any disarming way; rather, he seemed to just get tired in the way a fatigued professional boxer might eventually stop working out with a punching bag. Now, Dr. Taub, you're probably wondering why I had not retaliated and better defended myself since Rocco was smaller than I and I had, as I mentioned earlier, some experience as a pretty decent street fighter.

T: What did deter you from counterattacking?

K: First and foremost, my lifelong allegiance to the principle of self-preservation. I knew from the moment Rocco launched his attack that I could take him…easily. But I also knew that if I did, I would be on the Romans' hit list the very next day. And I just didn't have the guts or spine or balls or whatever other part of the anatomy one needs to expose oneself to an ambuscade carried out by a mob of future Tony Soprano henchmen.

T: But you said earlier that the Ukrainian lad had defended himself well against one of the Barbarians and came away with an elevated stature that served to protect him from the gangs.

K: Ah, but I also said that the Ukrainian, because he fought with fearless and ferocious abandon, was deemed by the gangs and practically everyone else as a nutcase who could, under conducive circumstances, actually kill an adversary. I was no such person and everyone, including the gangs, knew that. My preference would have been to fight Rocco with boxing gloves and beat the shit out of him in front of a crowd of schoolmates in the civilized manner of Gentleman Jim Corbett, as played by Errol Flynn in the movie *Gentleman Jim*. So I took a minute's worth of pummeling from crazy Rocco and came away from the humiliation to live many more years without facial scars or a damaged brain. I hope the same cannot be said for him.

T: You wish him dead, even now?

K: Certainly. You know, Dr. Taub, there has not been a week that has gone by since that hallway encounter with Rocco when I haven't at least fleetingly wished him dead. You might find it interesting to know that I have even had recurrent fantasies, one as recently as yesterday, of personally introducing him to the Grim Reaper.

T: What do you mean?

K: Well, the fantasy is something like this: through some Internet search I would find Rocco alive and learn of his whereabouts. If he hasn't done prison time, maybe he's a bank president somewhere or the Newark Chief of Police. Come to think of it, he might very well have been a bank president or police chief who earned a long-term residency in a penitentiary for on-the-job malfeasance. Anyway, I'd find his home and surveil it for a while, just to get the gist of his comings and goings. I'd pick a time in the evening when I knew he would be out on the street by himself. I'd sidle up to him and say in a friendly Errol Flynn voice, "Is your name

Rocco?" He would of course say yes. With that, I would introduce myself by name. A perplexed look of non-recognition would cross his face. To clarify matters, I would add, "Rocco, you and I had lockers next to each other at Cleveland Junior High School in Newark." I'd pause, seeing he was searching his memory for that odd, elusive factoid from the distant past. He seemed to extract nothing of value that would connect his past to mine so he just silently stared back, maybe thinking, for all I knew, that I was a class representative who hunted him down in order to invite him to our 53-year class reunion. Then I'd quietly drop a few reminders: "Rocco, you may not remember this but I accidentally bumped into you at the lockers. I apologized but you felt it necessary to punch me out until you grew tired. You hurt and humiliated me pretty badly. Is any of this coming back to you now?"

At this point Rocco's eyes would become luminous as he stepped into the light cast by an overhead street lamp. In my mind's eye they seem to radiate his belated recollection of the memory I had just conjured up for him along with an eerie dread of the late-night encroacher who had just interrupted his traverse to a safe place elsewhere in the neighborhood. He'd look up at me—he would not be much taller than he was at Cleveland but quite a bit stumpier—with wonder and suspicion and then say, "Wa, what do you want?" I'd reply, "I came to express my gratitude for the thrashing you gave me with your fists about 50 years ago. It was an act of pugilistic beauty and taught me something important about how a coward can take violent liberties with the rights of another human being providing he has the sanction and protection of a mob of other cowards." It was clear even on that darkened street that Rocco did not fully grasp some of the words and certainly not the sardonic tone of my remarks. He'd then say, "I, I, I have to be going. Take it easy." I'd step in front of him and say, "Rocco, don't leave until I give you my gift of gratitude." He'd hesitate and then ask, "What is it?"

It was then that I would hoist my right leg rearward into a punter's kicking position and then swing it full speed until my steel-tipped shoe squarely landed in the V of his crotch. He'd crumple like a soggy bag of potato chips onto the sidewalk and then I would pounce on him, banging my fists into his midsection until he lost consciousness and then I would finish him off by slamming his head into the concrete pavement. I'd then make my escape and never be discovered as the perpetrator of this dastardly deed. That's about it, Dr. Taub, that's my fantasy for the day.

T: That's quite a fantasy, to be sure. Dr. Kittleman, we will have to stop for today. I have, in response to hearing you recount this fantasy a couple of thoughts I'd like to leave with you. First, I'd like to know what that fantasy has meant to you in that you have relentlessly carried it with you for so many years, almost like an old, battered suitcase you daren't part with on your travels. In other words, is the fantasy more like an old, comforting friend or does it feel something like an intrusive nuisance, an unsightly and burdensome valise that you schlep around but would just as soon discard? Second, what did it feel like to you as you related the fantasy to me? And what do you imagine were my reactions to hearing how you fantasized your revenge upon Rocco?

K: I think the answers to those questions would make a good starting point for our next session. See you then.

Diary, I've resurrected that fantasy literally thousands of times over the years but never before to another person. I suppose I have considered it a much too horrific and immoral tale to trust that someone else could bear hearing it without registering revulsion and condemnation. Dr. Taub evinced neither emotion and yet I can never tell what is façade and professional persona, and what might be his genuine feelings about me. Are they in any significant way different from each other? I'd like to know.

What I do know is that my feelings have vacillated since telling him that fantasy. At times I am comforted and emboldened by the fact that he is privy to my quintessentially vindictive nature. But at other times I feel dangerously exposed and vulnerable to his judgment of me. This causes me greater anger that sometimes reaches the level of fury. In the midst of my rage my homicidal feelings toward Dr. Taub return and I become frightened that I will murderously enact them. I know enough about the therapeutic process from my readings to recognize that I am in the throes of an intense, negative transference and that I am, to use the explanatory terms of the psychoanalytic school, subject to regression and that regression can be "in the service of the ego"; in other words, a salutary stepping stone to mental health. Freud coined the term "working through" to suggest that the patient will need time, often considerable time, to introspect, contain, and understand powerful emotions and, if at all possible, change for the better. I still don't know whether this is possible. How does anyone, including Dr. Freud, know when the "working through" process will kick in well enough to prevent a madman like myself from regressing to the point of going berserk with rage? Each time Dr. Taub and I slowly safari through the dense, perilous thicket of my mental jungle I imagine myself to be about to reach the heart of darkness of a murderer. Diary, is that who I am? Whoops, I again forgot you are nothing but a coffee- and tear-stained piece of writing paper, incapable of consolatory responses. Fuck you, heartless diary.

Dr. Taub's Anamnesis 8/18/06

The patient recounted an experience of his physical and emotional victimization at the hands of a bully who pummeled him at a locker in their junior high school. It began with an accidental bump and ended with raw, uncontrollable, and degrading sadism at the hands of the bully. This traumatic experience was exacerbated by the patient's knowledge that he could and would have defeated the bully in a fair fight but for the fact that the latter had a battalion of fellow gang hoods standing at the ready to retaliate for any harm done to him. Thus, his pride was shattered and profound humiliation followed in its wake, even to this day. The episode, now a 50-year-old memory, perdures, recurrently rankling Professor Kittleman with its great intensity, persistence, and vividness. He has even mentally choreographed a fantasy in which he wreaks murderous revenge upon the bully when they meet as adults on a dark street outside the unsuspecting bully's home. Given the fact that over the years the patient has revisited this fantasy a myriad number of times without any harm eventuating, I am not overly concerned about the fantasy per se.

My question—my concern—is, however, whether Professor Kittleman, in divulging this fantasy to me, will experience some relief and escape from the clutches of his homicidal emotions and obsessions or whether the disclosure of the fantasy will, conversely, serve as kindling to his already highly inflamed vindictive feelings. And will I, by intentionally encouraging him to relive not only the capacious past but some of the primal murderous emotions that reside there, be witlessly laying the groundwork for my assassination? In other words, am I, by continuing to treat this patient, putting into place the tinder for my auto-da-fe?

K: Dr. Taub, I'll pick up where we left off and try to answer the questions you raised at the end of our last session. Unless, of course, you'd prefer to ask me something else.

T: No, please go right ahead.

K: Okay. I can't really determine whether my vengeful fantasy about Rocco and me is a friendly companion, a true-blue ally, that cleaves to me each time I become despondent over an emotional pummeling I receive in my topsy-turvy life. I suppose in some ways it must serve an adaptive, positive purpose. Why else would it visit me like an unbidden incubus in the night? So, to partially answer your question, Dr. Taub, I think this particular fantasy befriends and succors me in my battles with despair by casting me in the role of a heroic, victorious avenger who finally exacts justice by ridding the world of a stumpy piece of dung that deserves to be flushed into a sewer. In that respect the fantasy is uplifting and welcome and I can time and time again revel in the make-believe glory it affords me. But there is another side to all of this, Dr. Taub.

T: What is that?

K: Simply put, it is the recognition that, after all is said and done, it is merely a fantasy and nothing more. Soon after reveling over my imagined glory in smiting one of the lesser forces of evil on this planet, I must each time return to grim reality. And the yawning gap between the heroic figure in my fantasy and the pathetic person I really am beckons me and I am hurtled into that bottomless abyss of despondency that was once referred to by the old-time psychoanalysts as melancholia. So, Dr. Taub, my glorious fantasy is neither pure friend nor pure foe, but instead is an inclement-weather pal who shows up when I am in need of some sunshine in my life and drops me back into a downpour of drenching despair the moment I feel better about myself.

As for the matter of how I felt when I related this fantasy to you, that too was a mixed blessing. It is always a comfort to impart an intimate thought or memory to someone who can be trusted with it. In an important sense, sharing that painful memory of my hallway skirmish with Rocco feels sustaining because I draw sustenance from knowing that from now on I won't have to bear it alone. It feels really healing to know that that damaged part of my self is now organically a part of you. As a result, I may feel less alone whenever I have those painful memories of being Rocco's punching bag because I will know that my memories of that experience coupled with my fantasies of killing him will also become a distinguished inhabitant of your mental life. Maybe you can, in the manner the psychoanalytic school theorizes about when it refers to an intersubjective emotional process, "metabolize" my rage, transform it into something more benign, and ship it back to me in a less malignant and explosive package. You know, Dr. Taub, I'll bet that even the mythic Sisyphus could have used such help from a sympathetic sidekick who would eternally lend him a hand or a supportive word while he futilely pushed the heavy stone up the hill. If that was to be their absurd common fate for all eternity, they could at least draw existential comfort from knowing their plight was caringly and equitably shared. Do you think, Dr. Taub, you could be Sheldon Kittleman's steadfast helpmate while he repeatedly and absurdly pushes his own personal boulder to narcissistic heights?

T: I'll be your helpmate for as long as it is realistically possible, Dr. Kittleman. I can do no more than that, but my help may ultimately be indispensable to your welfare.

K: That at first sounded comforting until you qualified your remarks by adding the phrase "as long as it is realistically possible." Do you perhaps know what that phrase suggests to me?

T: No. What?

K: It suggests that you will stand by me until or unless you discover that I have become a certifiable menace to you. Do you realize, Dr. Taub, that not once in our previous session did you ever inquire about the extent of my homicidal urges toward you? You allowed me to prattle on about my absurd fantasy in which I conjured up a juicy scenario of wreaking revenge on Rocco, the budding Mafioso, for a 50-year-old attack he made upon my person and, worse, my adolescent pride. But you never checked in with me about the status of my constant hatred for you. Did you really think that my revisiting that hallway encounter with Rocco would relieve my anger and humiliation? And did you actually believe for one moment that my willingness to share with you that long-harbored fantasy of violently bloodying and killing Rocco on a city street would take care of the toxic anger I feel toward you or, for that matter, assuage my undifferentiated loathing for the rest of the world?

T: Not quickly or without complication, Dr. Kittleman. But time is an important dimension in therapy and I am trying to enlist your faith in a therapeutic process that, admittedly, ordinarily yields psychological rewards quite gradually or I suppose, when viewed from the impatient patient's perspective, glacially.

K: "Impatient patient." I like that. Do you know, Dr Taub, about the impatient patient who raced into his therapist's office announcing that he was overwhelmed by a fear that he was physically shrinking? In his panic, he besought the doctor for an immediate cure for his delusion. The good doctor responded by saying, "You'll just have to take a seat and be a little patient." Ah, I appreciate your chuckle in the midst of all this grotesquerie, Dr. Taub. Thank you. But I must return to the matter of my murderous thoughts, if you don't mind.

I can appreciate your petitioning me for more patience. But there are good reasons for my skepticism. First of all, recollections of painful, humiliating, and infuriating experiences will almost always ignite one's basest emotions. That's a psychological truism if there ever was one. Thus, a psychological visit to the original site of pain and humiliation will almost always arouse feelings of rage. The result, in the short run at least, is a feeling that one is being revictimized and retraumatized. Who, then, other than the most masochistic, martyrish nincompoop would seek or welcome such torture? There is one other matter I must mention in this regard, Dr. Taub. You may be of the opinion that the recollection and revivification of painful, long-dormant memories is a salutary, cathartic means of salving their malignant effects. I must tell you that so far that has not been the case with me and I will further explain why. Whenever I kill Rocco in my fantasy, I know that I have killed him strictly on some elusive imaginary level. I have not carried out a courageous vengeful act at all, other than in my thoughts. And, in my own Steinian way, I always know that a fantasy is a fantasy is a fantasy. I am thus forced to realize that one can never be truly heroic within the confines of a glorious fantasy in the way one can in actual life. My fantasy is a pitiful compensation, an escape from the odious recognition that I had one, and only one, opportunity to mete out justice to Rocco and I chose to dodge it out of cowardice. Reviving my fantasy does not bolster me, Dr. Taub; rather it trivializes my life and every recollection of it diminishes me. I hope you can understand that.

T: I can. But, as your therapist, I can use only the knowledge and therapeutic skills that I have at my disposal and that includes a search for roots and causes of psychological conflicts. For example, you seem to believe that I am inducing early memories simply for the sake of catharsis. That is not the case. That fantasy about killing Rocco contains much that is of great importance. You hate and despise yourself for "dodging" a fight with him. We need to know why you are so harsh and unforgiving toward yourself over something you had so little control over at the time, namely, your fears of being annihilated by a gang. Don't forget, you were nearly killed by a gang of kids carrying rock-laden sacks only a year or two before the encounter with Rocco. Surely, you must have stored away that terrifying memory in your mind so that it probably played a part in why you later surrendered to Rocco's blows. I believe you feel and think that you had no good cause to passively take his vicious punishment and have therefore attributed your behavior to cowardice. I think you need to understand your actions in the context of both your prior brush with a deadly gang and the certain reality that the Romans could have done some serious damage to you had you roughed up Rocco. I think, without question, you did the right and sensible thing by not taking him on, considering the circumstances.

K: Dr. Taub, I find your empathy consoling but there is a resistance I always feel whenever you reach out to me with understanding and insight. I suppose, given my narcissism, that I am compelled to feel that if there is any way to resolve my indecipherable conflicts I must be the primary cryptographer and captain and navigator of the good ship *Therapy* and any contribution from you, no matter how wise and empathic, is an interference.

In any case, given the fact that you insist upon serving as my flashlight-toting usher, escorting me time and time again to my seat in a dank, dilapidated theater to view the chilling horror movie that is my life, I have no choice but to hate you for your illuminating help. Perhaps you believe that I will one day come to enjoy and even laugh over the painful tableaus I see on that screen. If so, I need to disabuse you of that belief by letting you know that my anger is becoming more and more unbearable and may in a short time become uncontrollable and dangerous.

T: Is that how you feel now?

K: Not quite. But I do feel like I am on the verge of entering a new psychological realm, a place where I have never been before: sheer homicidal madness. Yes, in my youth, as you know, I could kill whole armies of ants with wrathful glee and abandon. As a matter of fact, I have always been quite a facile and eager killer of insects. Give me an attacking mosquito or fly and I will exterminate it with a swat or the spray of an insecticide without the slightest twinge of guilt or remorse. But until now I have always rigidly eschewed opportunities to carry out acts of violence against human beings.

T: I know how and why you avoided violence in dealing with Rocco, but by what other means did you manage to avoid violence?

K: Well, by staying away from military service, for one. I was too young to serve in World War II and the Korean Conflict, if that is the proper term for that war. During the all-too-brief interbellum years of the early '60s, I gained a temporary exemption from the draft by cozening a nice Jewish lady at the Newark draft board, who allowed me to take a three-month vacation in Europe. When I returned, she had evidently lost, misplaced, or intentionally disposed of my records, because I never heard from the draft board again. It's just one of those inexplicable, serendipitous flukes I will never understand. I consider myself eminently fortunate, however, because I never, until now, had a penchant for killing or being killed. Besides, our country no longer engages in morally defensible wars.

T: Dr. Kittleman, we're going to have to stop for today. Earlier in this session you criticized me for failing to question and assess the level of your dangerousness. I think that is a justifiable criticism. To avoid making the same mistake twice, allow me to ask you how safe you feel with your murderous urges right now.

K: I will answer that question, Dr. Taub, but first I must ask you: how safe do you feel with my murderous urges?

T: I can truthfully say that I trust you to return for another session without doing me any harm.

K: Fair enough. Your expression of confidence in me may be all the ballast I need to make it through yet another session. I'll see you then.

Professor Kittleman's Diary 8/26/06

Diary, was I lying to Dr. Taub when I told him I was harmless, albeit tenuously? I must have been. At this very moment I have
the urge to go right back to his office and kill him, if need be right in
front of one of his other patients. What is stopping me? Fear of legal
retribution in the form of a long stint in a penitentiary? Diary, I
don't think so. I know that if I kill Dr. Taub, a good and upstanding
man and an excellent therapist, I will turn my weapon upon myself
and live only seconds more than my hapless victim. Not to escape
incarceration, mind you, but because I have, by committing murder,
become nothing more than noxious refuse, a disgusting, disposable
nullity, a bestial being that kills simply to revel in the sheer blood-
thirstiness of killing in order to sate the basest of emotions, revenge
for emotional injuries inflicted by perpetrators other than my intended victim. How absolutely worthless my life has been! Wouldn't it
be fitting to end it by committing one final egregious act?

Dr. Taub's Anamnesis 8/27/06

The patient has pointed out, correctly, the need for a more focused assessment of his level of dangerousness. Although I don't consider him to be an imminent danger to me or others, he is now manifesting a greater degree of agitation and fear when discussing his murderous obsessions and urges, which is of course cause for concern. Perhaps it will be necessary, in order to stave off further decompensation, to refer the patient for a psychiatric evaluation in order to determine his need for a regimen of psychotropic medications. Yet I don't particularly favor this modality of treatment for this patient because I'd expect him to react adversely to such a recommendation. I'm quite certain that he would view my resort to medications as a sign that I am losing faith in the efficacy of the therapy to achieve psychological success. And he'd be right. I am beginning to doubt my personal and professional capacity to help this patient. Worse, I fear that he will progressively subvert my every attempt to help him—he pointed out in the last session how he must be the sole navigator of therapy—and the end result will be a colossal disaster for both of us. Perhaps it's time for me to acknowledge my own narcissism, accept my limitations, and admit to this desperate patient that I am doing him a terrible disservice by treating him. If I did, would he better accept me for being so self-effacingly human, or would he plunge even more deeply into despair over the discovery that the putative captain of the good ship *Therapy* is really Ensign Rudderless who is steering us both to the shoals of disaster? Perhaps the fact that I am admitting my fears and shortcomings to myself will do both of us some good. We'll see.

Eighteenth Session 8/31/06

K: As you can see, I'm not feeling well today.

T: Yes, you seem quite distraught.

K: I am. I think this will be our last session. I'm bursting at the seams with rage and I feel that I am on the precipice of launching a lethal attack upon the world. No, that is not quite accurate. I have spent most of the week brewing delicious schemes with which to kill you.

T: Would you care to tell me what they are?

K: No, I would not. They're scary enough as it is; I don't think I want to revitalize them with sanguinary descriptions. Isn't it enough that my diseased mind is now obsessed with plots to kill you? How can you just calmly sit there asking for my death-recipes as if I had just mentioned to you that I just discovered a new way to make spaghetti? That makes me think you are the crazier of the two of us.

T: Perhaps I should remind you that in a previous session you urged me to carefully monitor your level of dangerousness. I am doing that now. One reliable means for assessing dangerousness is to identify whether a patient has formulated a specific, concrete, and executable plan as well as recently acquired a dangerous weapon such as a gun for use in carrying out a lethal act of aggression. Another aggravating factor to be considered would be the excessive, judgment-impairing use of alcohol or drugs. What are your thoughts about these criteria I've just mentioned?

K: How can I honestly answer such a potentially entrapping question? I know that if I reply by saying that I have a plan and a weapon you will have me hospitalized. That is your professional right and duty. Well, the truth of it is that I have no weapon such as a bomb or gun. But I have amorphous images in my mind of doing to you what I did to Rocco in my murderous fantasy: bashing your skull against a concrete wall or sidewalk. Does that qualify me for the psychiatric hoosegow?

T: It might if you really feel that you cannot contain your urges to hurt me. How would you feel if I arranged for a temporary hospitalization at one of our local facilities? As a precautionary measure it would provide you with the safety and protection you might need from your own destructive impulses.

K: And protect you as well, Dr. Taub, from those same impulses?

T: All right, I'll concede that it would provide us both with an essential measure of protection. Yes, it would, I believe, be to our mutual advantage if you underwent a temporary hospitalization. I could remain your primary therapist during your stay and would visit you daily until your discharge, if you like. You'd receive a thorough evaluation and a needed respite from your worries about losing control of your murderous feelings and we'd resume the outpatient treatment upon your discharge. What do you think?

K: Dr. Taub, you know that the biopsychiatrists who run those units are big on medications. They'll prescribe them to virtually every patient regardless of diagnosis. They'll want to put me on their favorite prescription the moment I mention the catchwords "anxiety" or "depression." It provides them with something tangible, a silver bullet, to give their patients in order to compensate for the fact that most of them don't know a fucking thing about doing therapy and feel helpless because they can't effect an instant cure in the short time they are allotted with most of their in-patients. No thanks, Dr. Taub. I came to you for help, but if you are going to place me in the hands of others—pill-dispensing biopsychiatrists no less—I must assume that you've lost confidence in yourself. And there is no worse therapy than one in which a patient is treated by a therapist who doesn't believe in his own healing powers. I will not allow you to replace yourself with unscientifically tested, mind-numbing chemicals that will irrigate my bloodstream and further fuck up my brain. That feels too much like abandonment to me and serves only to fuel my hatred for you.

T: Would you cooperate with me if I, nevertheless, proceeded with a hospitalization plan under the 5150 mental health statute?

K: I would not. You know something, Dr. Taub? I just had a fleeting thought. I wonder if my persistent murderous feelings toward you have primarily represented, on the unconscious level of course, a test of your character, your moral courage. Week after week I have beleaguered you with hateful, vindictive feelings and, until now, you have withstood them with courage and conviction, knowing, I'm sure, that your patience and forbearance could cost you your life. You have demonstrated exemplary integrity and humanity in dealing with my *mishegaas*, Dr. Taub, at least until now. I realize that I have presented you with one of the most complicated and daunting of all therapeutic challenges a therapist could face: treating a patient who poses an imminent threat to your life. How are you supposed to treat such a monster? Well, you have, in my estimation, treated this monster with sensitivity and unwavering care, if my opinion of you counts for anything. As for me, what choice did I have other than to ensnare you with the mouth-watering blandishment that I would be a willing supplicant in search of a cure for an incurable malady? Any self-respecting therapist with a healthy ounce of narcissism would fall for a patient like me, much like the male spider falls into the treacherous web of the female spider that has cunningly enticed him to lose his head after sexual conquest. Please excuse the sexual overtones and decapitating violence of the analogy, Dr. Taub, but you get my drift. Yes, I, as the supreme narcissist, went in search of a therapist whom I could badger and bully with the supreme therapeutic challenge: to treat and cure me of a raging desire to kill him. What could be a more glorious narcissistic victory for you, Dr. Taub, than to effect such a miraculous cure? And what a glorious narcissistic victory for me that I would have allowed you to save me from the tragedy of committing murder and totally destroying my life.

Sadly, Dr. Taub, you ingloriously failed to meet the "supreme therapeutic challenge" by allowing your fears to invade the sacrosanctity of our bond, our therapeutic relationship, when you considered interning me in a hospital where I would be psychologically probed by a bevy of white-coated strangers seeking to discharge me from their midst as fast as possible by drowning me in the latest generation of untested psychiatric drugs.

Yes, Dr. Taub, you have ultimately failed to meet my challenge, my standard for character and moral courage. I of course realize that the standard by which I am judging you is impossibly high, grandiose by any ordinary ethical standard that gauges moral conduct, but as an unreconstructed narcissist, I claim the prerogative, the right, to be completely guided by my own lights. And now, Dr. Taub, without any further ado, I'm going to do what the devil won't do—that's an old Southern expression, I'm told—I'm going to leave you.

T: Excuse me. You've caught me by surprise. We still have time left in our session. I don't understand what you have in mind. We haven't resolved the matter of your safety and, of course, my own. Shall we hold to our schedule for next week's session? Can I trust you to remain under control until then? I ask these questions because your last comment carried a tone of finality. I'd like you to call me if you are experiencing intolerable feelings. I freely acknowledge that I disappointed and betrayed you by suggesting hospitalization but, as you know, I'm bound by the ethical strictures and requirements of my profession to consider such options in situations of this nature. I'm still very willing, however, to continue our therapy if you will give me another chance.

K: I'm sorry, Dr. Taub, but you know how unforgiving narcissists can be over even the flimsiest slights and lapses in other people. Goodbye, Dr. Taub.

T: One more moment, please. What are your intentions, then?

K: Here I must exercise another narcissistic prerogative. I will leave you to wonder and worry about my intentions. Goodbye.

Professor Kittleman's Diary 9/1/06

Diary, I'm engineering my own destruction. I prematurely quit therapy because my therapist was not perfectly attuned to my overarching needs and expectations. Now I feel completely alone, seething with rage that is being frayed by the minute. I have no one to turn to for help because I have excommunicated the only person I have ever really trusted since my wife died. My mind takes me on strange and circuitous journeys that terminate disastrously. There is, alas, no lofty escape that will take me from the depths of my mental suffering. I suppose I could immure myself in my home, live hermitically with my books and CDs and just wait until I die of natural causes. I could, on the other hand, end my worthless life more quickly by imbibing a poison that would at once induce eternal sleep. Come to think of it, I often feel tantalized by the beautiful tranquility of this game plan. Or, I could pursue a premeditated scheme to kill Dr. Taub. As always, I cleave to this obsession like a pit bull to his bone, though I know that I will not survive the murder of Dr. Taub for more than a few minutes. I have enough of a conscience to understand that murdering him will spell the end of my life as well—my suicide—with or without the use of poison. There it is, diary. I sit here writing in a state of emotional bondage, a captive of my unremitting despair, expressing my heartfelt feelings to your mute and cruel indifference. Fuck you—again—diary.

Dr. Taub's Anamnesis 9/1/06

Professor Kittleman has terminated his therapy abruptly and prematurely, defying and countermanding my attempts to have him continue in treatment until he gains greater control over his vindictive rage. He decamped in an angry and despairing mood and issued what might reasonably be considered a veiled threat: he will leave me to wonder and worry over whether he poses a threat to me. Not too surprisingly, he reacted adversely to my suggestion that his worsened, unsafe condition might warrant the intervention of temporary hospitalization. He foresaw, perhaps not entirely incorrectly, that he would be pressured to use psychotropic medications in an in-patient facility, a procedure which he perceived to be invasive and degrading. All in all, he regarded my suggestion to be a crass form of betrayal and rejection and bolted from therapy in rebellion, as he put it, over my loss of confidence in my own healing powers. As I see it, he had a valid point, although his reaction was disproportionate in that he gave me no slack, no opportunity to regain my confidence and rebuild our relationship. As is the case with narcissistic personalities generally, lapses and slights on my part were experienced by the patient as profoundly humiliating and demeaning injuries to his sense of self and thus he adjudged them to be entirely unforgivable.

The nebulous nature of the patient's current threat leaves me with little choice. Tomorrow I will contact one of our local law enforcement agencies and request that Professor Kittleman be taken into custody and placed in the psychiatric unit of Clark Hospital for observation and evaluation for a period of up to 72 hours under the stipulations of the California 5150 mental health statute. I realize that by undertaking this drastic measure I will have virtually disqualified myself as Professor Kittleman's therapist, but the particular exigencies of this situation—the imminent threat posed by the patient to me, himself, and the public at large—require me to relinquish my professional responsibility to him in favor of those community agencies that can more capably restrain and protect him from acting out his destructive obsessions.

SAN FRANCISCO CHRONICLE
September 6, 2006
SECTION B, PAGE 4
By Lowell Atkins
Chronicle Staff Writer

PSYCHOLOGIST SAVAGELY ASSAULTED
ON CITY STREET

Noted San Francisco psychologist, Dr. Arnold Taub, was assaulted late last night on a city street only two blocks from his psychotherapy office. Dr. Taub was evidently heading home from work when he was intercepted and savagely beaten by an assailant with a blunt instrument. Police officer Dan Stiles, who was summoned to the scene of the crime, reported that the assault was brutal enough to cause severe head injuries. Dr. Taub was rushed to San Francisco General Hospital where he remains in critical condition. Officer Stiles, and other police authorities who are investigating the assault, believe that robbery was not a motive for this attack since none of Dr. Taub's belongings had been taken from his person. Their tentative assessment leads them to believe that the assailant was either a deranged man who was wandering the street and came upon Dr. Taub by happenstance, or was someone with a serious grudge against Dr. Taub. Police officials request that anyone who can provide information leading to the identification and arrest of the assailant should contact them immediately at 555-429-2148.

Dr. Taub is the father of two teenage daughters and the husband of Sharon Taub, a sociology professor at the University of California, Berkeley. Ms. Taub, speaking from the bedside of her husband at San Francisco General Hospital, stated that, to her knowledge, her husband, a kind and gentle man, had made no enemies of the kind that would attack him so viciously.

SAN FRANCISCO CHRONICLE
September 8, 2006
SECTION B, PAGE 6
By Lowell Atkins
Chronicle Staff Writer

As Dr. Arnold Taub, the San Francisco psychologist, who last Tuesday was the victim of a brutal beating on a San Francisco street near his office, remains in critical condition at San Francisco General Hospital, the police are investigating every possible clue to this crime. Police officials have indicated that they have two possible leads: DNA evidence that may become available once blood samples taken from the scene of the crime can be analyzed, as well as the possible use of reliable third-party testimony that would serve as grounds for a warrant to inspect the files of one of his patients for inculpatory evidence. It is not known if Dr. Taub, who has been comatose since incurring severe head injuries, would, upon recovery, be able to identify his assailant. Thus far, police officials believe he may have been blindsided in such a manner that he would be completely incapable of making an accurate identification even if he recovers his memory of the attack.

THE SAN FRANCISCO CHRONICLE
September 11, 2006
SECTION B, PAGE 5
By Lowell Atkins
Chronicle Staff Writer

Police Chief Warren Spencer announced yesterday that an inspection of the files of one of Dr. Arnold Taub's patients based on a court-authorized warrant, coupled with DNA and other evidence, has provided a reliable lead to the identification of his assailant. Dr. Taub, who remains in a life-threatening coma at San Francisco General Hospital, was brutally beaten last week only a few blocks from his psychotherapy office. Police do not as yet have their prime suspect in custody, but are confident they will locate his whereabouts and apprehend him within a few days. The district attorney's office, which has been actively investigating this case since its inception, is planning to move forward expeditiously with arraignment proceedings.

THE SAN FRANCISCO CHRONICLE
September 15, 2006
SECTION B, PAGE 4
By Lowell Atkins
Chronicle Staff Writer

Police Chief Warren Spencer announced at a press conference yesterday that the suspected assailant of Dr. Arnold Taub, who was violently attacked over a week ago near his office in San Francisco, has been taken into custody and charged with the crime of attempted murder. Should Dr. Taub lose his life as a result of the attack, the alleged assailant would be charged with murder, according to Assistant District Attorney Nancy Taylor. Ms. Taylor stated that her office is still awaiting the results of DNA tests before officially announcing the identity of the alleged assailant and the full extent of forensic evidence that will be used to incriminate and convict him.

THE SAN FRANCISCO CHRONICLE
September 18, 2006
SECTION B, PAGE 1
By Lowell Atkins
Chronicle Staff Writer

The district attorney's office announced yesterday that it has collated unassailable forensic evidence with which to prosecute the suspected assailant of Dr. Arnold Taub, noted San Francisco psychologist, who was assaulted on a city street near his office almost two weeks ago.

The corpus of forensic evidence, according to Assistant District Attorney Nancy Taylor, includes a compelling DNA matchup based on blood samples taken from the scene of the crime that virtually rules out anyone else, reliable third-party testimony that assisted her office in securing a court-authorized warrant to access the files of one of Dr. Taub's patients (the suspect), and, perhaps most tellingly, the suspect's almost immediate voluntary verbal confession to the police, who quickly secured a written confession along with his motive.

The alleged assailant is Dan Simmons, a longtime vagrant and petty thief of the streets of San Francisco with an extensive criminal record. According to court records, he was mandated by the courts several years ago to enter psychotherapy and referred to Dr. Taub. He then, while still in therapy with Dr. Taub, mugged and robbed an elderly woman on a city street, and was arrested and charged with the crime. He enlisted the services of Dr. Taub to appear in court as an expert witness in order to have him attest to his psychiatric condition in hopes that Dr. Taub's testimony would provide evidence of extenuating circumstances that would mitigate the penalty for his crime. It did not. Dan Simmons was sentenced to a four-year term of imprisonment at San Quentin State Penitentiary. According to court records, corroborated by notes in Dr. Taub's files, as Mr. Simmons was being forcibly removed from the courtroom by sheriffs' deputies he shouted out, "I won't forget this, Taub. Sooner or later I will f__ing kill you." According to Ms. Taylor, soon before being paroled from San Quentin about two weeks ago, he disclosed to a fellow inmate that he lived for the day when he would be free so he could, first thing, exact his revenge upon Dr. Taub. The inmate, evidently harboring hopes for a commutation of his own sentence or a boost in his prison privileges in exchange for his testimony—colloquially known as jailhouse snitching—upon learning of the assault, reported Simmons' verbalized death threat to prison authorities, who in turn transmitted this important information to the district attorney's office. It was information that was essential to the investigation, since it provided the primary basis for the court-ordered warrant to vet Mr. Simmons' file in Dr. Taub's office, in which Dr. Taub allegedly referred to Mr. Simmons in the last pages of the file as a sociopathic menace to society and a veritable threat to himself.

A heartening footnote to this story is the fact that Dr. Taub is no longer in a coma or in critical condition. According to San Francisco General Hospital spokeswoman, Sylvia Goodman, he is expected to make a full, albeit gradual, recovery from his injuries. He has evidently reported to police authorities that he indeed had an opportunity to identify Mr. Simmons moments before the attack and would be entirely willing to attest to that fact in court as soon as he is physically able. According to Ms. Taylor, Mr. Simmons, if convicted of this crime, would undoubtedly serve a very long prison sentence based upon his cumulative criminal history and the particularly violent nature of the assault upon Dr. Taub.

A Telephone Conversation, September 22, 2006

K: Doctor Taub?

T: Yes. With whom am I speaking?

K: Sheldon Kittleman. How are you? I was so sorry to hear about your misfortune.

T: Thank you. I'm much better now and hope to be out of the hospital before not too long and back to work as soon as I can. Do you think you'd be interested in returning to therapy, Professor Kittleman? Is that why you've called?

K: Not exactly. I have a favor to ask of you, Dr. Taub. I definitely will not be returning to therapy. Ever. But I would like to visit you in the hospital for one last and very brief get-together, if you don't mind. If having me in your hospital room gives you the jitters, I'm perfectly willing to see you in the company of other people.

T: That won't be necessary. If convenient, come over tomorrow at three o'clock.

K: I'll be there. Thanks.

A Hospital Visit, September 23, 2006

K: Thanks for seeing me. How are you feeling?

T: Do you know about the two psychologists who met on the street? They greeted each other by saying, "You're fine, how am I?" But since I don't really know how you are, I'll just say I'm doing okay considering the reason for my being in this hospital. The staff here treats me very well. Since I'm pretty fatigued, though, I can have only short visits, so please tell me why you wanted to see me and I'll do my best to respond in a helpful manner.

K: Sure. First I wanted to thank you for the care and consideration with which you conducted the therapy. It is much appreciated despite the fact that I truly believe it did not do me an ounce of good. I am, alas, a stone-hearted ingrate and not even now can I acknowledge that the therapy was the least bit therapeutic.

T: Why then are you appreciative of my help?

K: Because you are a truly decent person and there are too few such individuals in the world. In that respect memories of my sessions with you will be emotionally sustaining.

T: I'm glad to hear it. But how have you fared since our last session?

K: Well, right after that session I suspected that you might be siccing the police on me under the 5150 statute, so I left town. But not empty-handed, I must add. I took with me my full collection of Laurel and Hardy tapes. I probably never told you this, but I have tapes of practically all their films, some specially ordered from an archival service in Los Angeles. I first began seeing their movies at the Laugh Theater on lower Market Street in Newark, New Jersey, when I was about 10 years old. They also showed the movies of Charlie Chaplin, Ben Blue, Fatty Arbuckle, the Three Stooges, and the crossed-eyed Ben Turpin (you know, he insured his eyes with Lloyds of London against uncrossing) that were so funny that I came out of that theater with red eyes and a hacking cough from laughing so hard. For 25 cents you could see about five hours' worth of the best comedy of that bygone era.

Years later I purchased the films of Laurel and Hardy and would go back to them time and time again, playing them on my VCR whenever I needed a picker-upper. And it always worked. So I schlepped my whole collection of Stan and Ollie along with me to a remote motel in Calaveras County and, holed up there, watched their movies for about 30 hours over the course of four days. When I left I was in good spirits and, aside from the deep emotional dip I took when I learned of your assault, I have been in good shape ever since.

T: In other words, Laurel and Hardy could achieve more in four days than I could over the course of several months in raising your spirits?

K: Not exactly, Dr. Taub. I remember often thinking while I was watching their hilarious films that you are probably a person who would also enjoy the comic absurdity of their zany skits. And when I left the motel I felt closer to you and much, much closer to the best, most remissive moments of my childhood, those many hours I spent at the Laugh Theater in Newark. I'm going to leave now, Dr. Taub—for good. But I would like to ask you one personal question before I do.

L: What's that?

K: Was I right or wrong? Do you enjoy Laurel and Hardy?

T: Absolutely. How about that scene from the *Music Box*, where they haul the piano up a steep flight of steps over and over again, not knowing they could have taken their horse-drawn wagon to that same destination with no trouble at all. Or, what about *Liberty*, their side-splitting movie where Stan walks in spasms because he has a live crab in his pants and the boys perform high-altitude antics on the steel beams of an unfinished skyscraper. That's some of the funniest stuff I have ever seen. And I'm sure you've seen *Blockheads*, that masterpiece of comedy, in which Stan remains in a World War I trench under orders to guard it, orders he patriotically fulfills until 1938, when he discovers to his astonishment that the war has been over for 20 years. He comes home, is feted as an eccentric hero in the newspapers, and takes residence at a veteran's facility where he ensconces himself in a wheelchair by folding one of his legs under his hips. When Ollie, who has read the newspaper accounts of Stan's heroics, finds his friend in a wheelchair ostensibly missing one of his legs, he is aggrieved and immediately dedicates himself to the preposterous task of carrying the completely ambulatory Stan to his car; no easy matter, to say the least. After a few inevitable mishaps, Ollie suddenly realizes that Stan has two legs after all and has needlessly put him through a physical ordeal for nothing. What follows is, in my estimation, the funniest dialogue in all of filmdom. An exasperated Ollie says to Stan, "Why didn't you tell me you had two legs?" To which Stan replies, "You didn't ask me." Then Stan self-pityingly blubbers to himself, "I've always had two legs. I didn't think…" I can see from your expression, Professor Kittleman, that we share a special affection for these two zany characters, Laurel and Hardy, and their exceptional humor, which, I suppose, means that you and I, through our common love of absurd pratfalls such as theirs, also share a deep appreciation for each other, each in his own ill-disguised way, if I may say so.

K: "Absurd pratfalls." I recall having had one of those not very long ago. Perhaps I can find a way to appreciate and find humor even in that scandalous mishap whenever I remind myself that were it not for that awful experience, we would never have met. Thank you, Dr. Taub. I'll remember what you've just told me, always.

T: You take care, Professor Kittleman.

K: I shall.

About the Author

Gerald Amada, Ph.D., was one of the founders and a director of the City College of San Francisco Mental Health Program and is now retired after a thirty-year career at that college. He has also recently retired from a thirty-five-year private psychotherapy practice. He is the author of ten books in the fields of psychotherapy and college student conduct. One of his books, *Anker's Plight*, is a somewhat autobiographical novel. *Professor Kittleman's Therapy* is his second novel.

Dr. Amada lives in San Rafael, California, with his wife, Marcia, and their dog, Chatchke. Readers who wish to contact him may do so through his website: geraldamada.com.

If you enjoyed this book
check out our other
film-related titles at
www.midmar.com
or call or write for a
free catalog
Midnight Marquee Press, Inc.
9721 Britinay Lane
Baltimore, MD 21234
410-665-1198
(8 a.m. until 6 p.m. EST)
or MMarquee@aol.com

Made in the USA